AMAZING
STRUCTURES

Written by
Michael Pollard

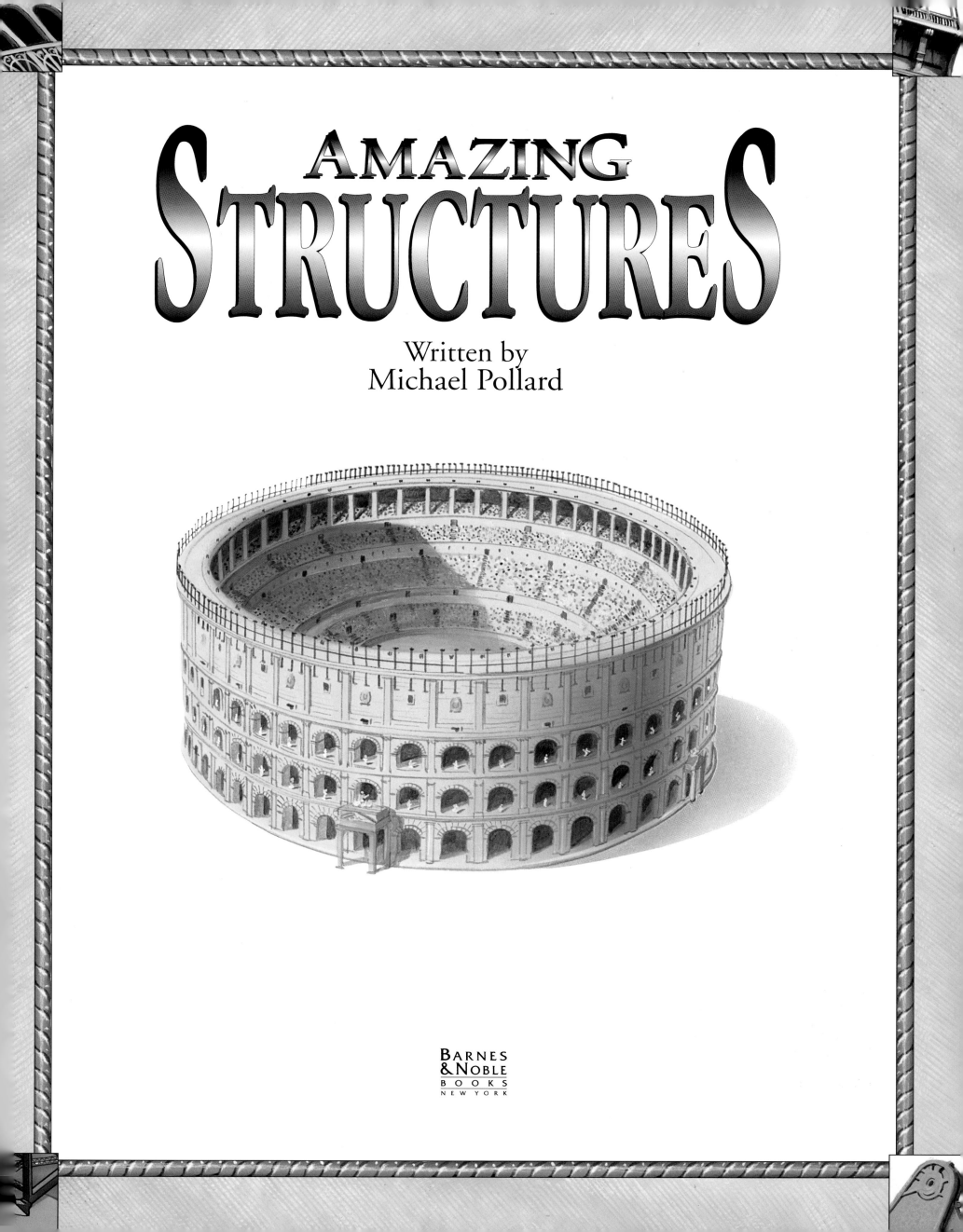

BARNES
&NOBLE
BOOKS
NEW YORK

ACKNOWLEDGMENTS

Illustrated by

Julian Baker, Bob Corley (Artist Partners), Robert
Farnworth, Dave Higginson (Northern Art
Collection), Steve Noon (Garden Studios), Julia
Osorno, John Rogers (Ian Fleming & Associates),
Roger Stewart (Kevin Jones Associates), Andrew
Wheatcroft (Virgil Pomfret Agency), Sean Wilkinson.

*The Publishers would also like to thank the following for
their assistance*
Blackpool Pleasure Beach Ltd
Eiffel Tower archivist
Empire State Building
Jodrell Bank, for information on the VLA Radio Telescope
Statoil, for information on Gullfaks C
Thames Barrier Publicity
United States Information Service at the American Embassy, London
Vale Royal Borough Council, for information on the Anderton Boat Lift
Wirth Howden Tunnelling for information on the Channel Tunnel

This edition published by
Barnes & Noble, Inc., by arrangement with
Andromeda Oxford Limited

1996 Barnes & Noble Books

Planned and produced by
Andromeda Oxford Limited
11–15 The Vineyard
Abingdon
Oxon OX14 3PX

Copyright © Andromeda Oxford Limited 1996

ISBN 0-7607-0290- X Amazing Structures
M 10 9 8 7 6 5 4 3 2 1

Printed in Italy

Contents

What is a structure?

A structure is an object that has been designed and built for a special purpose. Thousands of years ago, people built the world's first structures, their homes, out of the branches and leaves of trees. As they learned to make and use tools, they began to build larger structures using a wider variety of materials. Places of worship were among the first large structures to be built. The ancient Egyptians built temples in which to worship their gods. They also worshiped their rulers and built huge palaces for them to live in. When Egyptian rulers died, they were buried in pyramids with their treasures alongside them.

Many modern structures such as skyscrapers, oil rigs and space stations have been built as working environments. Others, like tunnels and bridges, carry roads or railways. Another group of structures, including the Eiffel Tower and Statue of Liberty, were built as monuments to celebrate important events. Over the centuries of human history, large structures from the Great Wall of China to today's structures in space mark the achievements of gifted designers, builders and craftspeople.

PLACES OF WORSHIP

Temples and churches are mostly grand structures with domes, towers or spires that soar up toward the sky. During the twelfth and thirteenth centuries, there was a great surge of cathedral building in the Christian countries of western Europe. With their lofty vaulted roofs, buttressed walls and high arches, the new cathedrals achieved a splendor that had not been seen in Europe before.

Copper outer coating

Original iron framework

Two spiral staircases

MONUMENTS

For thousands of years monuments have been built to commemorate events, such as victory in battle, or the achievements of well-known people. Memorials and statues are a familiar sight in many towns and cities, and some statues are famous worldwide. The Statue of Liberty, which stands in New York Harbor, was erected to celebrate the hundredth anniversary of the United States' independence from Britain.

BUILDING A STRUCTURE

No matter how much machinery is available, a skilled workforce has always been essential for building a structure. The pyramids of ancient Egypt were built over 4,000 years ago, by a huge force of workers who labored for years to build them, using only the simplest hand tools. Over 70 pyramids have survived – a tribute to the ancient Egyptians' building skills.

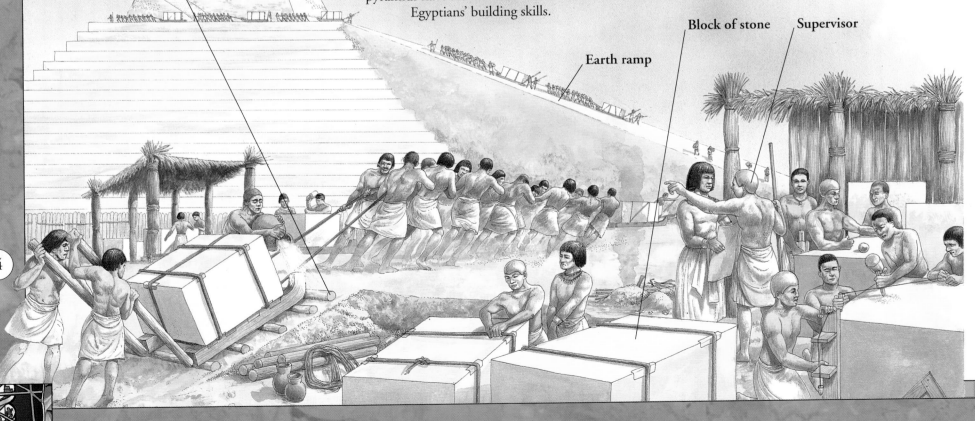

Wooden rollers

Earth ramp

Block of stone

Supervisor

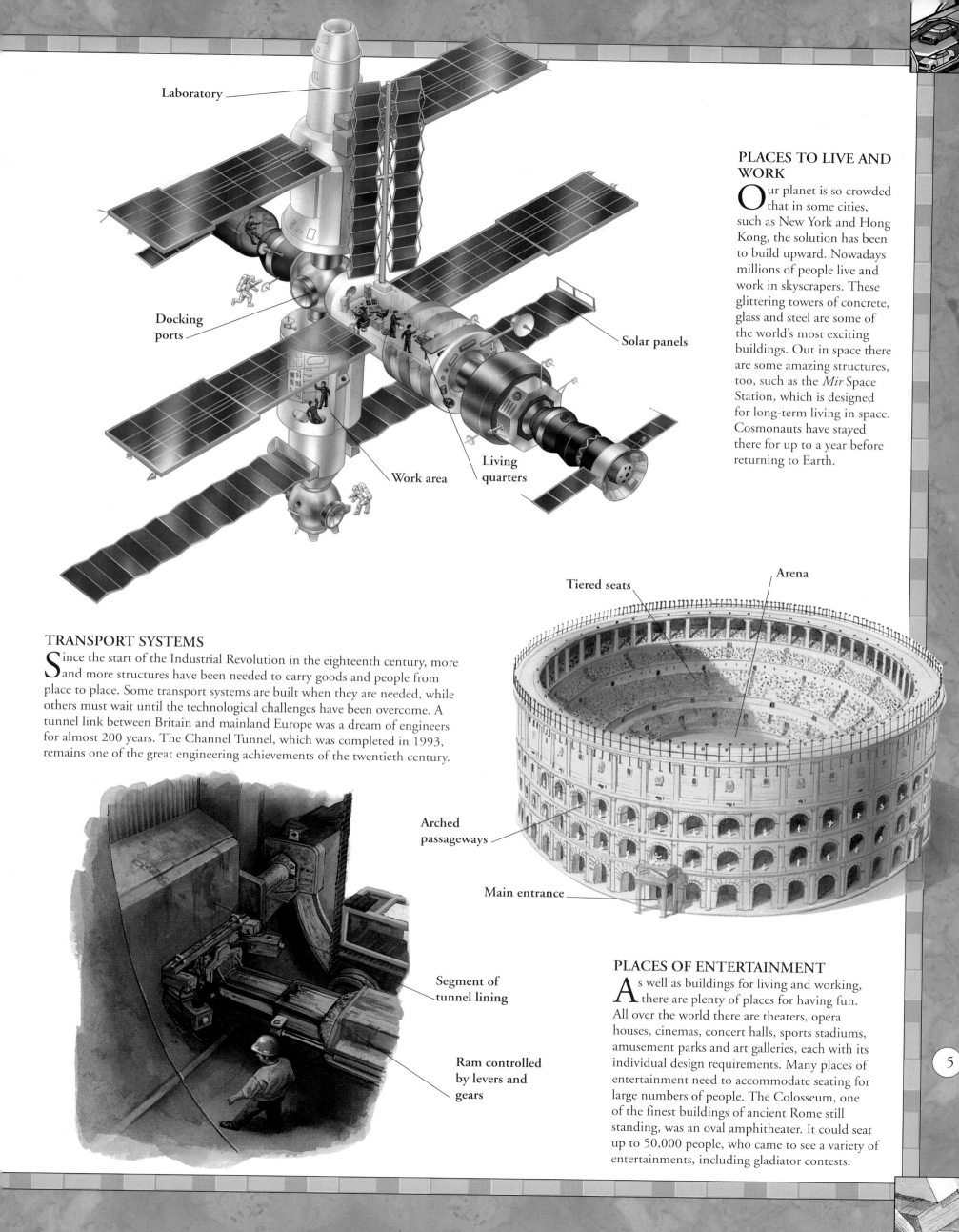

Laboratory

Docking ports

Work area

Living quarters

Solar panels

PLACES TO LIVE AND WORK

Our planet is so crowded that in some cities, such as New York and Hong Kong, the solution has been to build upward. Nowadays millions of people live and work in skyscrapers. These glittering towers of concrete, glass and steel are some of the world's most exciting buildings. Out in space there are some amazing structures, too, such as the *Mir* Space Station, which is designed for long-term living in space. Cosmonauts have stayed there for up to a year before returning to Earth.

TRANSPORT SYSTEMS

Since the start of the Industrial Revolution in the eighteenth century, more and more structures have been needed to carry goods and people from place to place. Some transport systems are built when they are needed, while others must wait until the technological challenges have been overcome. A tunnel link between Britain and mainland Europe was a dream of engineers for almost 200 years. The Channel Tunnel, which was completed in 1993, remains one of the great engineering achievements of the twentieth century.

Segment of tunnel lining

Ram controlled by levers and gears

Tiered seats

Arena

Arched passageways

Main entrance

PLACES OF ENTERTAINMENT

As well as buildings for living and working, there are plenty of places for having fun. All over the world there are theaters, opera houses, cinemas, concert halls, sports stadiums, amusement parks and art galleries, each with its individual design requirements. Many places of entertainment need to accommodate seating for large numbers of people. The Colosseum, one of the finest buildings of ancient Rome still standing, was an oval amphitheater. It could seat up to 50,000 people, who came to see a variety of entertainments, including gladiator contests.

Development of structures

The history of large structures shows how the development of new materials and the invention of tools enabled designers and builders to take on new challenges. Until about 200 years ago, stone, brick and wood were the main building materials. From about 1800, iron and then steel were increasingly used in large structures. The twentieth century brought the use of reinforced and prestressed concrete, as well as a variety of plastics. All these materials made new kinds of structures possible.

STONEMASONS' TOOLS

This selection of ancient stonemasons' tools includes: a square (1) and a variety of mallets, wedges and chisels (2). A favorite material for making tools before the Iron Age was a hard stone called dolerite. Stone tools did not keep their edge for long, so stonemasons had teams of helpers to resharpen their tools and make new ones.

SCULPTING

Large stone structures such as those of the ancient world lent themselves to decoration with patterns, figures and inscriptions carved painstakingly out of the stonework. The sculptor's craft was highly valued.

DESIGN CHANGES

Designers have always looked for ways of improving structures. The first lengths of the Great Wall of China were made of earth, but when the Emperor wanted a stronger wall, the design was improved to include stone foundations, with stone and brick walls and a brick walkway along the top.

MAKING BRICKS

Bricks were first used in places where stone was hard to find or difficult to transport. The first bricks were tablets of clay and straw that were allowed to harden in the sun. Soon it was found that bricks were stronger if the clay was baked in a fire or an oven. A mortar made from mud was used to hold the bricks in place.

GOING UP

Throughout recorded history, mankind has constantly developed new building materials, and invented new building techniques, to create ever more impressive structures.

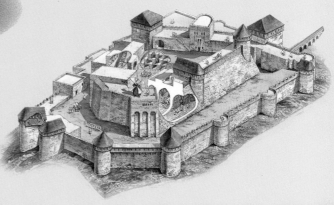

1779: First use of iron in structural building in a bridge at Ironbridge, England

1818: Marc Isambard Brunel invented the tunneling shield, which was first used to tunnel under the Thames River in London.

c. 2565 B.C.: Completion of the Great Pyramid at Giza

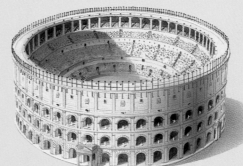

A.D. 72–80: The Colosseum in Rome was an early example of the use of arches to carry great weights, enabling tall structures to be built.

1170: Krak des Chevaliers, Syria, a huge Crusader Castle, featured hidden passages and 28-foot (8.5-meter) thick walls.

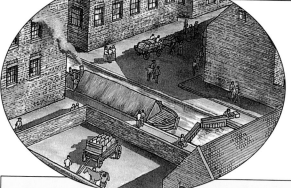

WELDING AND RIVETING

The Industrial Revolution in the nineteenth century opened up new opportunities in construction. The use of iron and steel meant that ways had to be found of joining pieces of metal together. Two of the methods used are welding (1) and riveting (2).

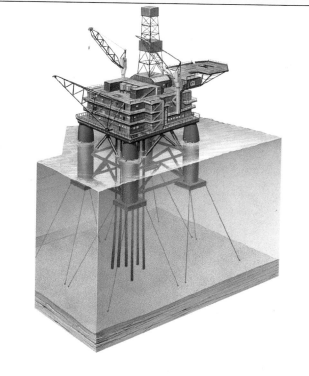

① ②

CRANES AND CANTILEVERS

Tower cranes lift materials, or even complete modules for a high-rise building, into place. They work on the same principle as a cantilever bridge, where the weight on one end of a beam supports the other end.

NEW CHALLENGES

From the 1960s onward, the discovery of oil from reserves under the sea presented structural engineers with new challenges. They had to design oil rigs that would resist salt-water corrosion and stand up to stormy weather in open water. Oil rigs are massively built, with a steel framework attached to a heavy concrete base secured to the seabed.

TUNNELING

The history of modern tunnels began in 1818, when the tunneling shield was invented, making it possible to tunnel through soft ground. In 1861 compressed-air drilling machines were introduced, followed in 1867 by dynamite, a more efficient explosive.

1868: Reinforced concrete invented when Joseph Monier, a French gardener, strengthened concrete by incorporating iron rods

1885: World's first steel-framed building, the Home Insurance Building in Chicago, was built. Although only ten stories high, it is recognized as the world's first skyscraper.

1889: Architecture and engineering combined to create France's Eiffel Tower, a riveted iron structure.

1970s: The discovery of undersea oil and gas reserves resulted in the building of giant ocean platforms hundreds of feet tall that can withstand the fiercest storms.

1986: The Russian space station, *Mir*, was transported into orbit by spacecraft and assembled piece by piece by cosmonauts.

1993: Completion of the Channel Tunnel, the largest-ever construction project in Europe

Great Pyramid

MAGIC EYE

The Egyptian sun-god, Horus, was worshiped and feared by the ancient Egyptians, and his symbol, the magic eye, was used to ward off evil. The first pyramid, built as a burial place for King Djoser in about 2630 B.C., was thought to represent a huge stairway for the king to climb to join the sun-god Horus in the sky.

In ancient Egypt between 2630 B.C. and 1640 B.C., when a pharaoh or his queen died, their mummified bodies were placed in stone tombs called pyramids. The Egyptians believed that the spirits of the dead would travel from these tombs to the next world. At 485.5 feet (148 meters) high, the Great Pyramid at Giza, near modern-day Cairo, is the tallest of the Egyptian pyramids, and the oldest of the Seven Wonders of the Ancient World. The Great Pyramid is the tomb of King Khufu, sometimes called by his Greek name, Cheops. No one knows the exact dates of Khufu's birth and death, but the Great Pyramid, which was built in readiness for his death, was finished in about 2565 B.C.

Khufu's Pyramid was built from more than two million blocks of stone and may have taken 20 years to build. The stone was brought by boat from the quarries, and then dragged to the site on sleds. Thousands of people worked on the building. The laborers were not slaves, but free Egyptians who worked on the pyramids as an act of worship to their king. They worked during the time of year when the land near the Nile River was flooded and no farming could be done.

Capstone

Casing

Mediterranean Sea

EGYPT

Red Sea

Nile River

Mediterranean Sea

Nile Delta

Giza (2) (1)

EGYPT

Nubia

NILE VALLEY

The civilization of ancient Egypt grew up along 620 miles (1,000 kilometers) of the fertile Nile River between Nubia and the Nile Delta, where the river flows into the Mediterranean Sea. For almost 4,000 years, the Great Pyramid (1) was the tallest structure in the world. Beside it is the carved stone figure of the Sphinx (2).

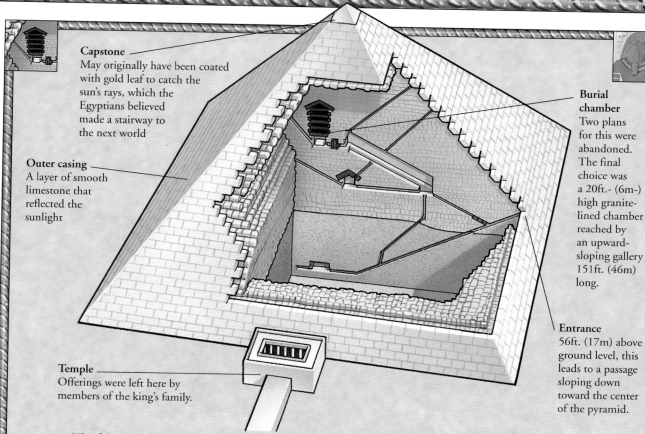

Capstone
May originally have been coated with gold leaf to catch the sun's rays, which the Egyptians believed made a stairway to the next world

Outer casing
A layer of smooth limestone that reflected the sunlight

Burial chamber
Two plans for this were abandoned. The final choice was a 20ft.- (6m-) high granite-lined chamber reached by an upward-sloping gallery 151ft. (46m) long.

Entrance
56ft. (17m) above ground level, this leads to a passage sloping down toward the center of the pyramid.

Temple
Offerings were left here by members of the king's family.

Khufu's Pyramid contains 2.3 million blocks of stone. The largest block weighs 15 tons, but most are about 2.5 tons in weight. Each side is 764ft. (233m) long at the base of the Pyramid. The base covers more than 12 acres (5 hectares) of ground.

ROBBERS

The pharaohs of ancient Egypt were buried with their personal belongings. These included jewelry, gold ornaments and richly decorated furniture. About 500 years after Khufu's death, robbers broke into the pyramids and stripped them of their valuables. They even tore open some of the mummies to expose the kings' bodies, which then decayed.

Wooden scaffolding

Ramp

THE SPHINX

The Great Pyramid is one of three large pyramids at Giza. Completing the group of monuments is the great stone lion with a human head, known as the Sphinx. Experts once thought that the Sphinx's head had been given the features of Khufu's son Khafre, who was buried in the second large pyramid. But they now think that the Sphinx may actually be much older than the Great Pyramid. The figure, which is over 187 feet (57 meters) long, was possibly intended to guard the entrance to the Nile valley.

BURYING THE PHARAOH

The burial of a pharaoh began with the arrival of his body by boat at a temple on the Nile. From there, priests led the mourners to the pyramid entrance and then through passages to the burial chamber. When the pharaoh's mummified body had been arranged with his treasures, the burial chamber was sealed with blocks of stone.

Great Wall of China

"It is a supremely wonderful sight! To think that these walls, built in apparently inaccessible places, are the work of man makes it seem like a dream."
Ludovic Herbert, *A Voyage Round the World*, 1872

Throughout history, until recently, China's northern borders have been the target of attacks by invaders from the mountains to the north. The Great Wall of China is evidence of the Chinese Empire's long struggle to defend its northern provinces. It is by far the longest wall in the world, with its main length and side branches totaling more than 3,730 miles (6,000 kilometers).

The wall was begun about 300 B.C., when the first separate parts, made of earth, were built by warring states across areas vulnerable to raiders. Then, in 221 B.C., the first emperor of a united China ordered these short lengths to be transformed into a continuous stone wall. A force of 300,000 slaves took 20 years to complete the task. Soldiers were posted in the watch-towers that were placed about every 330 to 650 feet (100 to 200 meters). From there, a close watch was kept for raiders from the north, and a chain of beacons could be lit to warn troops of impending danger. During the rule of the Ming dynasty (1368 to 1644), the Great Wall was rebuilt in the form in which it survives today.

Archer

BUILDER'S MARK

The inscription on this brick records that it was made in the twelfth year of the reign of the Ming emperor Wan Li, which was 1585. The Ming dynasty's efforts to strengthen the wall did not prevent an invasion by the Manchus, who took over China in 1644.

BUILDING THE WALL

The Great Wall was built by slaves working in terrible conditions, supervised by soldiers. Much of it passes through desert, and sandstorms often interrupted the work. Temporary walls had to be built to keep sand out of the foundations. Food supplies often ran short when bandits attacked the supply wagons, but the slaves were forced to keep working. If they fell sick they were simply thrown into the foundations and building continued over their bodies. The same fate awaited anyone who made a mistake or failed to work hard enough.

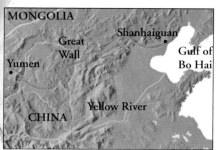

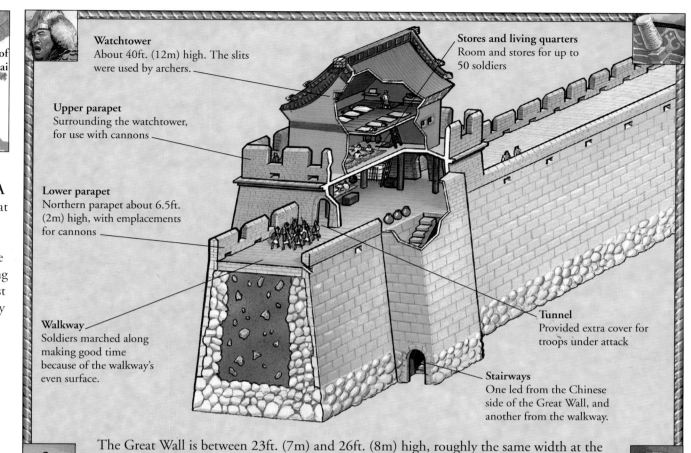

Watchtower
About 40ft. (12m) high. The slits were used by archers.

Stores and living quarters
Room and stores for up to 50 soldiers

Upper parapet
Surrounding the watchtower, for use with cannons

Lower parapet
Northern parapet about 6.5ft. (2m) high, with emplacements for cannons

Walkway
Soldiers marched along making good time because of the walkway's even surface.

Tunnel
Provided extra cover for troops under attack

Stairways
One led from the Chinese side of the Great Wall, and another from the walkway.

The Great Wall is between 23ft. (7m) and 26ft. (8m) high, roughly the same width at the base, tapering to about 16ft. (5m) at the top. Its stone foundation is 5ft. (1.5m) thick.

FROM MOUNTAINS TO SEA

The Great Wall's western end is at Yumen, high in the mountains of northwest China. It follows the hilltops and high ground, giving the troops who manned it a commanding view. The Great Wall finishes almost 1,240 miles (2,000 kilometers) away at Shanhaiguan on the Gulf of Bo Hai, an inlet of the Pacific Ocean. The spine of the Great Wall has a series of branches striking off to the south, marking the efforts of successive rulers to defend their borders.

Paved roadway

Scaffolding

Foot soldier

ATTACK!

Most of the time the Great Wall formed an effective defense against disorganized bands of raiders, who were outnumbered and easily fought off. But in the thirteenth century a ferocious and efficient army under the Mongol emperor Genghis Khan breached the Great wall with battering rams, heavy catapults and gunpowder. Genghis Khan's army of 250,000 horsemen was famous for its cruelty – all enemy prisoners were killed – and its determination to win.

The Mongols swept on to conquer China, and stayed for nearly a hundred years. After the Mongols were finally driven out, the emperors of the Ming dynasty rebuilt and strengthened the existing Great Wall, and extended it.

FIRST EMPEROR

Qin Shih Huang Ti (259–210 B.C.) was the first emperor to rule over all of China. It was during his reign that the short lengths of earth wall that already existed were rebuilt and incorporated into a new continuous stone wall. The Great Wall became a symbol of the unity of the new China under Emperor Qin. When he died, he was buried in a huge tomb with a "terra-cotta army" of 7,500 life-sized model soldiers to guard him. These models were not seen again until 1974, when the tomb was discovered near Xi'an.

11

Colosseum

"Hail, Caesar, those who are about to die salute you."
The gladiators' greeting to the emperor, A.D. 80–523

GLADIATOR'S HELMET

A heavily armored gladiator was called a murmillo. He wore a metal helmet with a sturdy ridge along the top to protect his skull from blows. It also had a grille at the front, which protected his face but meant that his vision was not as good as his opponent's.

The ruins of the Colosseum in Rome still stand – despite many fires, earthquakes and military attacks – as a reminder of the great days of the Roman Empire nearly 2,000 years ago. The huge oval amphitheater, which was completed in A.D. 80, could seat up to 50,000 people. It was used for a variety of spectacular entertainments, including gladiator contests, chariot races and even a mock sea battle, for which the whole arena had to be flooded.

The name Colosseum comes from the Latin word *colosseus*, meaning "gigantic". It probably refers to the amphitheater's vast size, as well as to the colossal statue of the emperor Nero that stood nearby. The foundations were made from concrete and the huge main structure from stone, with four levels of columns on the outside. Inside, the seats were tiered so that everyone had a good view of the arena. Underneath the wooden floor of the arena was a vast network of passages, with dens for the wild animals and rooms for the gladiators and other performers.

ARMED COMBAT

Gladiators were usually slaves captured in war. They were trained to fight to the death. The various types fought each other using different kinds of weapons. A retiarius gladiator carried a three-pronged spear and used a net to trap his heavily armored opponent, a murmillo gladiator.

BUILDING THE AMPHITHEATER

The Colosseum took a large work force of slaves over 10 years to build. It was started in A.D. 70 by the emperor Vespasian, but he died a year before it was finished. It was completed and opened by his son Titus in A.D. 80. Two years later the emperor Domitian added a fourth story.

Scenery above hoist

75 tiers of seats

Sand-covered floor

RAISING THE ROOF

The Colosseum's sun canopy was probably raised from the floor of the arena using ropes. It was hauled up using 80 sets of pulleys and winches installed at the top of the building.

Sun canopy
Spectators were protected from the weather by an awning measuring 73,000 sq. ft. (6,782 sq. m).

Seating
The emperor and his friends sat at the front. Above him sat the nobility, then merchants, foreigners and slaves. Women sat right at the top.

Arena
The wooden floor, measuring 282 ft. (86 m) long and 177 ft. (54 m) across, was covered with sand to absorb any blood.

Vaulted arcades
On three stories arched passageways ran around the outside of the amphitheater.

Famous Romans
In niches on the outside walls were statues of Roman emperors and famous citizens.

Entrance
There were 76 numbered gate-ways and four main entrances. Tickets were free, and showed a gate number.

Under the arena
Nine sections of branched tunnels connected numerous rooms and animal dens.

The Colosseum measures 613 ft. (187 m) across at its widest point, and was almost 164 ft. (50 m) tall. It was badly damaged by an earthquake in 1231.

ANIMAL SLAUGHTER

The killing of wild animals by gladiators was a popular sport. On the Colosseum's opening day, some 5,000 animals were slaughtered. They included lions, tigers, elephants and leopards. The animals were brought up from below the arena in a cage balanced with a counterweight, and they were released through trap doors for their final fight. Criminals were also killed by being hurled into the arena to be eaten by lions.

Emperor's box

Herald

Anderton Boat Lift

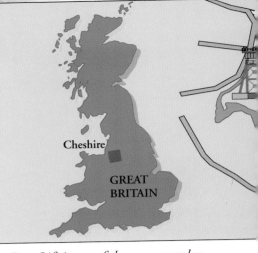

Cheshire

GREAT
BRITAIN

"The Anderton Boat Lift is one of the seven wonders of British waterways."
Robert Aickmann, *The Story of Our Inland Waterways,* 1955

There are three ways of enabling canal and river boats to change levels. The most common method is to use a lock, in which the water level is raised or lowered to move a boat from one level to another. The second way is to haul a boat over rollers. The third is to use a vertical lift. The Anderton Boat Lift in northwest England is the only surviving example of a vertical lift in Britain. It is one of only eight such lifts in the world. Although it is no longer used, there are plans to restore it.

The lift carried boats between the Weaver River, and the Trent and Mersey Canal over 49 feet (15 meters) above. When it first opened in 1875 it was operated hydraulically, but it became unsafe and in 1908 a new lift, described here, was installed. This lift worked in a simple, but ingenious way. Cast-iron weights balanced the weight of the tanks and meant that gravity provided most of the power. A small electric motor provided the rest.

PULLEY SYSTEM

Each boat-carrying tank was suspended on wires that ran from the tank over pulleys down to a set of cast-iron weights. These were equal to the weight of the water-filled tank. The tank was raised or lowered by turning the pulleys one way or the other.

Pulley

Cast-iron tubular column

SALT CHUTES

There were three large salt works near the site of the boat lift. Traffic on the Weaver River depended on exporting salt and importing coal and china clay. Salt from the canal boats at the top of the lift was poured down chutes to the river barges waiting below.

14

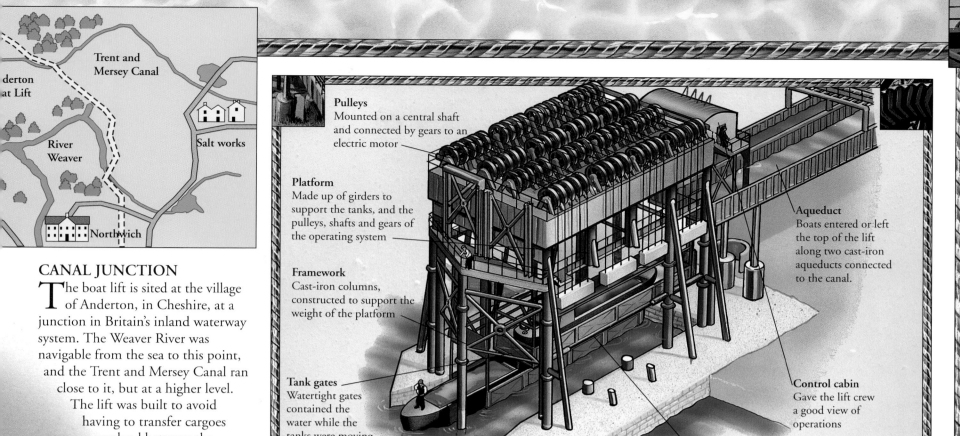

CANAL JUNCTION

The boat lift is sited at the village of Anderton, in Cheshire, at a junction in Britain's inland waterway system. The Weaver River was navigable from the sea to this point, and the Trent and Mersey Canal ran close to it, but at a higher level. The lift was built to avoid having to transfer cargoes overland between the two waterways.

Pulleys
Mounted on a central shaft and connected by gears to an electric motor

Platform
Made up of girders to support the tanks, and the pulleys, shafts and gears of the operating system

Framework
Cast-iron columns, constructed to support the weight of the platform

Tank gates
Watertight gates contained the water while the tanks were moving.

Aqueduct
Boats entered or left the top of the lift along two cast-iron aqueducts connected to the canal.

Control cabin
Gave the lift crew a good view of operations

Tanks
Each measured 75 x 15ft. (22.9 x 4.7m).

The Anderton Boat Lift raised and lowered boats 50ft. (15.3m) between the two water levels. The lift was powered by a 30hp motor. When full, each tank weighed about 252 tons.

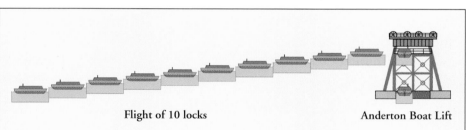

Flight of 10 locks   Anderton Boat Lift

LOCKS VERSUS LIFT

A series of locks to carry traffic between the Weaver River and the Trent and Mersey Canal would have taken far more space than was available. A flight of 10 locks would have been needed. The lift provided a much faster, more efficient way of connecting the two waterways.

TWO-WAY TRAFFIC

Two aqueducts allowed traffic to pass to and from the lift and the Trent and Mersey Canal. They were long enough, at 164 feet (50 meters), to allow boats to wait for the lift without holding up traffic on the canal. There were docks at the top where boats could take on cargo and supplies.

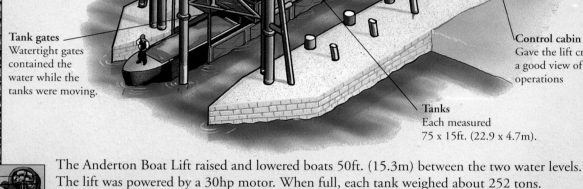

PULLEY POWER

The second lift was built over the top of the original Victorian structure. Tubular cast-iron columns formed the framework (1). These had to be strong enough to take the weight of two water-filled tanks (2) and their counterweights (3). Each tank was counterbalanced by its own set of weights so that it could be operated independently. Operations at the lower, river end were controlled from a cabin at the foot of the lift, and this was connected by a signaling system to the main control room at the top.

Statue of Liberty

*"Here at our sea-washed, sunset gates shall stand
A mighty woman with a torch, whose flame
Is the imprisoned lightning, and her name
Mother of Exiles."*
Emma Lazarus, *The New Colossus*, 1883

Torch

Travelers arriving by boat at New York Harbor are greeted by the magnificent sight of the Statue of Liberty, rising 300 feet (91.5 meters) above the water. Liberty stands on a small island, but from a distance she seems to be rising from the waves. The statue was a gift from the people of France, to mark the hundredth anniversary of the United States' Declaration of Independence in 1776. The work of the French sculptor Frédéric Auguste Bartholdi, it was made from sheets of beaten copper fixed to a central iron framework designed by Alexandre Gustave Eiffel, who later designed the Eiffel Tower in Paris. The statue was assembled in France and then taken apart, each piece carefully numbered, for the sea voyage to New York in 1885. The pedestal on which Liberty stands was paid for by American citizens, but difficulties in raising the money delayed the completion of the project for over a year. The statue was finally dedicated by President Grover Cleveland on October 28, 1886. It was the tallest structure to have been built since the Pyramids. The statue has now stood for over a hundred years as a symbol of freedom.

LIBERTY'S TABLET

July 4, 1776, written in Roman numerals on the statue's tablet, was the date when the United States of America issued its Declaration of Independence from Britain. War had already broken out between British and American forces, and fighting was to last until 1781. The Americans were aided by France.

BUILDING THE STATUE

The first sections to be made were the hand and torch. From a one-third-scale clay model a full-scale plaster copy was made. This was covered with a framework of wooden slats to make a mold. Thin copper sheets were then beaten into shape around the wooden mold and secured with one rivet in ten, so that the Statue could be easily dismantled for shipping to America.

LIBERTY ISLAND

The island on which the Statue of Liberty stands was formerly called Bedloe's Island. It was the site of a fort that commanded the entrance to the port of New York. It was renamed Liberty Island in 1956. From 1892 to 1954, people coming to live in the United States passed through an immigration center on nearby Ellis Island.

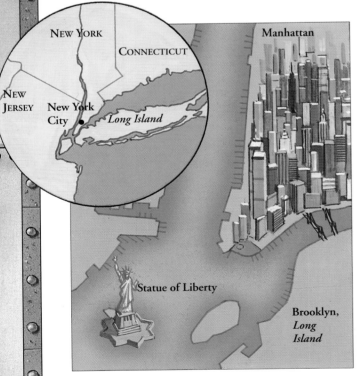

NEW AMERICANS

Between 1870 and 1910, over 18 million immigrants arrived in the United States from Europe, fleeing poverty and persecution. They included millions of Russian and Polish Jews who were driven out of their own countries. From 1886 onward, the Statue of Liberty welcomed them to their new lives of freedom.

Copper outer skin

Tablet

Right arm
42.6ft. (13m) long, contains a 54-rung ladder leading to the torch

Torch
A cluster of 1,000-watt bulbs inside the red and yellow glass flame shines across the harbor at night.

Crown
The seven spikes represent the seven continents and seven seas of the world.

Lookout
Observation platform inside the crown can hold 30 people. It is no longer open to visitors.

Skeleton
An iron framework (later replaced with stainless steel), attached to a central core of four wrought-iron posts

Tablet
Measures 23.6ft. (7.2m) long and 13.4ft. (4.1m) wide

Outer skin
300 overlapping copper sheets fastened by 300,000 copper rivets. The copper sheeting weighs over 90 tons.

Spiral staircase
Two 168-step spiral staircases lead from pedestal to crown.

Pedestal
151.5ft. (46.2m) high, standing on an 11-pointed, star-shaped base

The Statue itself is 148.6ft. (45.3m) high, and the pedestal is 151.5ft. (46.2m). The Statue weighs almost 204 tons. The pedestal's concrete foundation used 24,000 barrels of Portland cement.

HELP AT HAND

Liberty has suffered badly from corrosion. A chemical reaction between the iron rods and the copper skin caused the rods to swell up and rivets to break off, weakening the structure. In a major restoration project of the 1980s, every iron rod had to be replaced with new ones made from stainless steel.

Eiffel Tower

"Just because we are engineers does not necessarily mean that we give no thought to beauty in our constructions, or that in making something solid and long-lasting we ignore elegance."
A. G. Eiffel, replying to criticism of his Tower, 1887

When the Paris Exhibition of 1889 was being planned to celebrate the centenary of the French Revolution, the organizers held a competition for the best design of a tower to act as a focal point. There were over a hundred contestants, and the winning design was by Alexandre Gustave Eiffel.

Construction began on January 29, 1887, and was completed just over two years later. The Eiffel Tower's 12,000 iron parts were factory-made, drilled for rivets and numbered, before being brought to the site for assembly. Eiffel was an engineer rather than an architect, and his design reflected the latest engineering technology of his day. The tower was originally 984 feet (300 meters) high, but in 1957 television aerials were added, raising the height to 1,045 feet (318.7 meters). During its construction the tower aroused fierce controversy. A group of artists and writers described it in a Paris newspaper as "a dizzily ridiculous tower dominating Paris like a huge, black factory chimney." But it was a great success with tourists, and nearly two million people visited it in the first five months after it opened.

Third floor

Second floor

First floor

Decorative arch

LIGHT SHOW

From 1925 to 1936, the French carmaker Citroën sponsored a display of lights, using 250,000 colored bulbs, on the Eiffel Tower. The Citroën name could be seen shining from three sides of the tower up to 24 miles (38 kilometers) away.

GOING UP

Five hydraulic elevators, like the one above, were originally fitted. Four went up to the first and second floors, and the fifth took visitors from the second floor to the top. Today, two hydraulic and two electric elevators travel to the first and second floors. Two more elevators take visitors on up to the third floor.

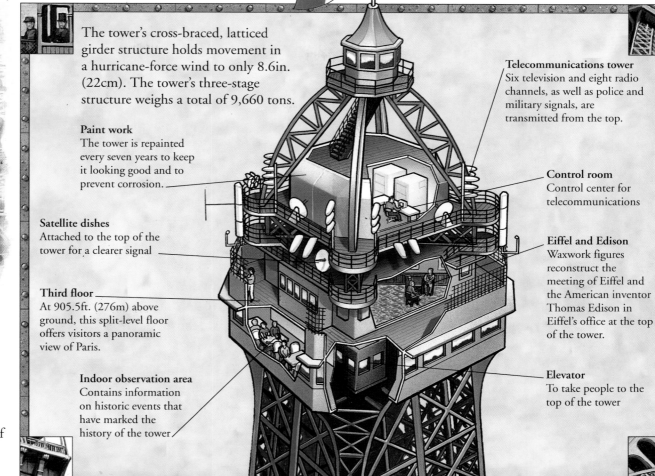

The tower's cross-braced, latticed girder structure holds movement in a hurricane-force wind to only 8.6in. (22cm). The tower's three-stage structure weighs a total of 9,660 tons.

Paint work
The tower is repainted every seven years to keep it looking good and to prevent corrosion.

Satellite dishes
Attached to the top of the tower for a clearer signal

Third floor
At 905.5ft. (276m) above ground, this split-level floor offers visitors a panoramic view of Paris.

Indoor observation area
Contains information on historic events that have marked the history of the tower

Telecommunications tower
Six television and eight radio channels, as well as police and military signals, are transmitted from the top.

Control room
Control center for telecommunications

Eiffel and Edison
Waxwork figures reconstruct the meeting of Eiffel and the American inventor Thomas Edison in Eiffel's office at the top of the tower.

Elevator
To take people to the top of the tower

ROOFTOPS OF PARIS

The top of the Eiffel Tower gives a fine view over Paris. But elevators were not installed in time for the opening ceremony in March 1889, and guests had to climb to the top up a 911-step spiral staircase, since removed. Not all of them made it, but Eiffel did, and proudly hoisted the French flag from the top.

(1) (2) (3) (4) (5)

STAGE BY STAGE

The tower was built in stages, each floor in turn providing a working surface for the floor above. The elevator tracks were fitted as work proceeded, and were used to carry cranes. The foundations were finished in June 1887 and by November the legs were well under way (1). The first floor (2) was completed on April 1, 1888, the second floor (3) on August 14, and the third floor (4) by December of the same year. The top of the tower (5) was completed on March 31, 1889.

ELEPHANT WALK

The Eiffel Tower, in its history of over a century, has been the scene of many famous stunts. Daredevil human visitors have included parachutists, trick cyclists and tightrope walkers. In 1948, the oldest female elephant in the world, aged 85, was taken for a long, slow walk up as far as the first floor by her owner.

Empire State Building

"The Empire State Building stands today as the greatest monument to ingenuity, to skill, to brain power, to muscle power, the tallest thing in the world today produced by the hand of man."
Alfred E. Smith, opening the Empire State Building in 1931

On August 29, 1929, New York newspapers reported plans for a new building on Fifth Avenue in the heart of Manhattan. Work was to start on the Empire State Building, planned to be 1,250 feet (381 meters) high, with 102 stories. It would be the tallest building in the world. Constructing a building of this size on a restricted site amid the bustle of New York's business district posed huge challenges. But the workmen labored around the clock – they even ate on the job – and the Empire State Building was opened on May 1, 1931. It had been built in just 15 months.

The Empire State Building is more than an office block. It is a major tourist attraction. Visitors can take an express elevator to the observatory on the 86th floor, which welcomes thousands of tourists a day. There is another observation platform on the 102nd floor. The Empire State Building held its title as the world's tallest skyscraper until 1973, when it was overtaken by the twin towers of the World Trade Center – 102 feet (31 meters) taller – in Manhattan.

MOVIE STARDOM

Almost as soon as it was built, the Empire State Building became a movie star. In the 1933 fantasy film *King Kong*, the giant ape fought on top of the building against American Army Air Force fighters before he was shot down.

AIRSHIP MAST

At the time the skyscraper was designed, airships seemed the most likely means of long-distance air travel, so a mooring mast for airships was fixed to the top of the building. But high winds made mooring too dangerous, and the scheme was abandoned. The mast became instead a housing for telecommunications antennae.

MEN AT WORK

The riveting gangs put together the steel frame at a furious pace. The casual way they rode the girders without hard hats or safety harnesses would not be allowed today!

Radio and TV
mast transmits
to four states

Art deco shell decoration

Windows:
6,500 in total

**102nd floor
observatory**
At 1,250ft. (381m)
high, it offers
views of five states.

86th floor observatory
Ships at sea more
than 37mi. (60km)
away can be seen
from here.

Outer walls
Made of 199,951cu. ft.
(5,662cu. m) of Indiana
limestone and granite

The lobby
Rising three stories high, it is
paved with European marble.

Basement
Provides car parking,
and houses the air-
conditioning and waste-
disposal systems

Staircase
There are 1,860
steps from street
level to the
102nd floor.

Offices
For some 20,000 people,
employed by 650 companies

Elevators
73, enclosed in 6.8mi.
(11km) of elevator shaft

The steel-framed
building took one
year and 45 days
to complete, and
measures 1,454ft.
(443.2m) to the top
of the lightning rod.
It weighs 308,000
tons. Visitors number
over 2.5 million
each year.

EMERGENCY!

On July 28, 1945, a
nightmare came true.
An aircraft crashed at full speed
into the Empire State Building, causing
$1 million worth of damage. It was a B-
25 bomber with a crew of two; both men
were killed. Another 12 people inside the
building died. If it had not been a Saturday
the death toll would have been much higher.
The causes were never explained.

WORLD'S TALLEST BUILDINGS

The tallest office buildings
without a mast are the
Petronas Towers in Kuala
Lumpur. But taller still because
of their masts are the Ostankino
TV Tower in Moscow at 1,761
feet (537 meters) and the C. N.
Tower in Toronto at 1,814
feet (553 meters).

1. Eiffel Tower, Paris, 984ft. (300m).
2. Chrysler Building, New York, 1,046.5ft. (319m).
3. John Hancock Center, Chicago, 1,125ft. (343m).
4. Empire State Building, New York, 1,250ft. (381m).
5. Sears Tower, Chicago, 1,453ft. (443m).
6. Petronas Towers, Kuala Lumpur, 1,483ft. (452m).

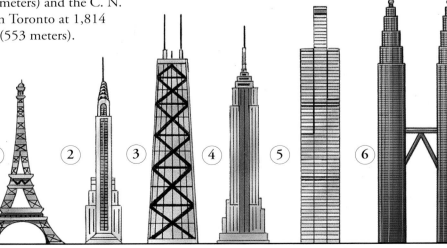

1 2 3 4 5 6

Sydney Harbor Bridge

"Constructed in the cantilever method with the half-arches held back by steel cables, [it] is undoubtedly the most celebrated and most massive bridge of its kind."
David J. Brown, Editor, *Ove Arup Journal*, 1993

MEETING POINT

The moment came in September 1930 when the two halves of the arch met in the middle. Onshore cables supporting the two halves were slackened off slowly so that the pieces sank into place against each other.

This giant steel-arch bridge is so wide it carries eight road lanes, two railway tracks, a cycle track and a pedestrian walkway across Australia's Sydney Harbor from Dawes Point to Milson Point. At 160 feet (48.8 meters) wide, it is the broadest long-span bridge in the world. The deck of the bridge is supported by steel cables, called hangers, suspended from an arch of steel girders and plates. All the steel components were made in Britain and assembled in workshops near the bridge site. The sections were floated into position on the water and then lifted into place by cranes standing on the growing arch. The bridge was designed to give 170 feet (52 meters') headroom to ships passing beneath it.

Design work began in 1923, building started in 1927, and the bridge was opened for traffic in 1932. To answer any public concerns about its safety, 72 railway locomotives weighing a total of almost 550,000 tons were shunted onto the bridge while structural checks were carried out.

DANGEROUS WORK

Laborers worked high above the water with few safety precautions. They had no protective clothing or helmets, and no guardrail either. Several men died during the bridge's construction.

Pylon

Upper chord

Lower chord

Hanger

Deck

CROSSING THE WATER

Steel cables supported the two halves of the bridge as they were built toward each other (1). The cables also had to support the weight of the cranes that lifted the arch sections into position (2). When the arch was complete, the steel hangers were lowered into place (3), followed by the sections of the deck (4).

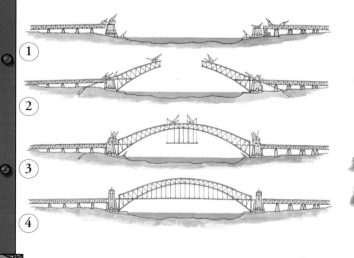

1
2
3
4

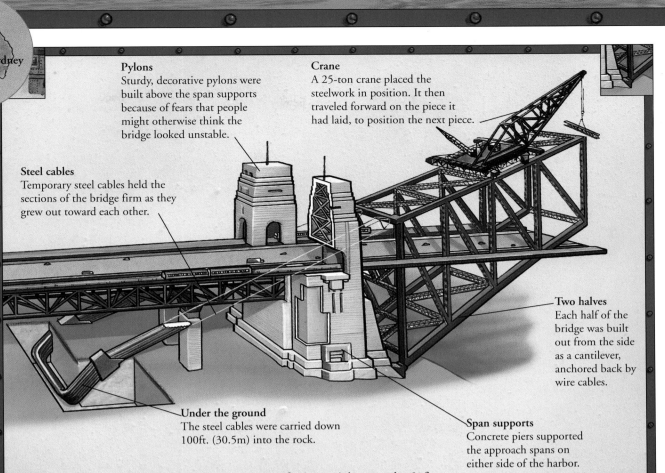

Pylons
Sturdy, decorative pylons were built above the span supports because of fears that people might otherwise think the bridge looked unstable.

Crane
A 25-ton crane placed the steelwork in position. It then traveled forward on the piece it had laid, to position the next piece.

Steel cables
Temporary steel cables held the sections of the bridge firm as they grew out toward each other.

Two halves
Each half of the bridge was built out from the side as a cantilever, anchored back by wire cables.

Under the ground
The steel cables were carried down 100ft. (30.5m) into the rock.

Span supports
Concrete piers supported the approach spans on either side of the harbor.

NATURAL HARBOR

Sydney is Australia's largest city and chief port, and capital of the state of New South Wales. This bustling city of 3,699,000 people stands beside one of the world's great natural harbors. The Harbor Bridge was built as part of a program to improve the city's communications without harming its shipping trade.

Sydney Harbor Bridge measures 1,670ft. (509m) long and 160ft. (48.8m) wide. Its single steel arch weighs 28,000 tons.

Approach span

BRIDGE TYPES

There are several types of bridge construction. These include a suspension bridge, which hangs from cables that run over the tops of towers (1); a cantilever bridge, built out in sections, with each section fixed at one end (2); and a steel arch bridge (3), such as the Sydney Harbor Bridge.

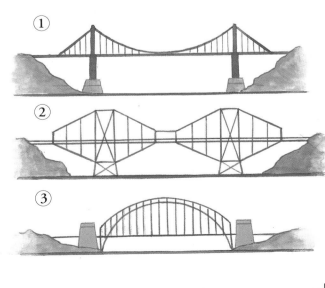

① ② ③

V LA Radio Telescope

From a site on the plains of New Mexico in the United States, 27 large metal dishes continuously sweep space for signals from the stars. The dishes make up the VLA (Very Large Array) Radio Telescope operated by the United States National Science Foundation. Unlike optical telescopes that give a visual image, radio telescopes pick up radio waves sent out by objects in space. Many of these objects are too distant to be seen with an optical telescope. The weak radio signals are amplified and recorded so that they can be studied by astronomers. Since about 1960, radio astronomy has transformed scientific ideas about the nature and size of the universe.

The VLA Radio Telescope was opened in 1980. Its metal dishes, which all focus on the same object, are arranged in the shape of a Y. They are connected electronically so that their signals can be combined. The effect is the same as one huge dish 17 miles (27 kilometers) in diameter.

"The great radio telescopes and optical telescopes have discovered objects of a type unknown only a few years ago. Some of these lie in the remote parts of space and time and convey to us on Earth records of the early history of the universe."
Sir Bernard Lovell, pioneer radio astronomer, 1974

SUBREFLECTOR

The purpose of the subreflector is to collect radio waves bounced off the parabolic dish and focus them. This provides a signal strong enough for the receiver to amplify and interpret. A strong signal is needed to overcome the problem of radio noise – interference from other objects in space or from radios and televisions.

Metal dish

Subreflector

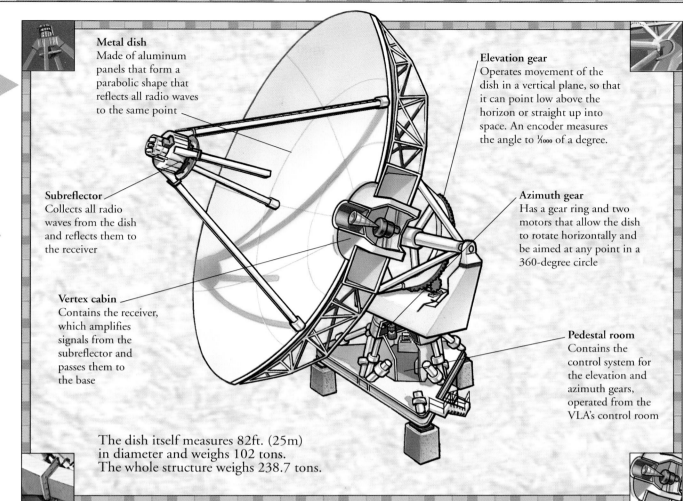

VLA SITE

The VLA site (1) is 50 miles (80 kilometers) west of Socorro, on the plains of San Augustin (2) in southern New Mexico. The site was chosen carefully. It is far enough south to enable radio astronomers to study 85 percent of the sky both north and south of the equator. On the flat desert ground, it is easy to make full use of the mobility of each dish.

Metal dish
Made of aluminum panels that form a parabolic shape that reflects all radio waves to the same point

Elevation gear
Operates movement of the dish in a vertical plane, so that it can point low above the horizon or straight up into space. An encoder measures the angle to $\frac{1}{1000}$ of a degree.

Subreflector
Collects all radio waves from the dish and reflects them to the receiver

Azimuth gear
Has a gear ring and two motors that allow the dish to rotate horizontally and be aimed at any point in a 360-degree circle

Vertex cabin
Contains the receiver, which amplifies signals from the subreflector and passes them to the base

Pedestal room
Contains the control system for the elevation and azimuth gears, operated from the VLA's control room

The dish itself measures 82ft. (25m) in diameter and weighs 102 tons. The whole structure weighs 238.7 tons.

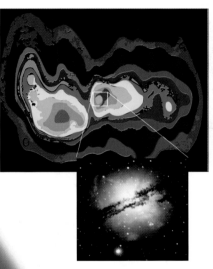

Centaurus A   M 82

COLLECTING WAVES

Radio signals have to be collected over a large area and brought into focus. The parallel radio waves bounce off the bowl-shaped dish (1) to a subreflector (2). From there, the waves are reflected again to the receiver (3), which amplifies them and converts them into electrical signals.

RADIO MAPS

Signals received by the VLA's dishes are used to build up maps of distant galaxies. In some cases a radio telescope can detect features that are much more extensive than the part seen through an optical telescope. This is the case with the galaxy Centaurus A. Only a small part of it – partly obscured by dust – is visible through an optical telescope (bottom left). The radio map (top left) covers a much wider area and gives a more accurate picture of the galaxy. With the galaxy M 82, the optical image (top right) is larger than the radio source. The radio waves come from the central part of the galaxy. This indicates that a hydrogen gas outburst took place one to two million years before our present view of the galaxy, which is 8.5 million light-years away.

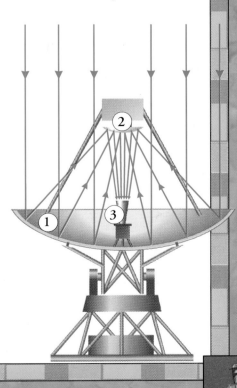

NASA

Shuttle launch site

INTO SPACE

The United States' space program is controlled by the National Aeronautics and Space Administration (NASA). Its duties include organizing manned spaceflights, orbital satellites and unmanned space probes to the planets.

The space shuttle is a rocket-powered spacecraft designed to return to Earth after each mission and be reused. The United States launched its first shuttle in 1981, from the Kennedy Space Center at Cape Canaveral in Florida. In the next ten years, another 37 shuttle missions lifted off from the same launch complex. The shuttle is made up of three parts. The crew and their cargo travel into space in an orbiter. This rides on a huge external fuel tank that detaches after takeoff and burns up as it re-enters the atmosphere. Two solid-fuel rocket boosters also drop away after use and parachute to Earth, to be recovered and reused.

The launch site also contains a huge vehicle assembly building where the shuttle parts are put together. A control center is on-site, together with design and testing facilities, and a 15,000-foot (4,572-meter) long landing runway.

CRAWLER-TRANSPORTER

A giant crawler-transporter, moving at no more than 1 mile per hour (1.6 kilometers per hour), carries the shuttle over 3 miles (5 kilometers) from the assembly building to the launch pad. The crawler-transporter moves on eight caterpillar tracks, each one over 9.8 feet (3 meters) high. It travels on a specially built road surface that sinks as the transporter passes over it, but springs back into place afterward.

Lightning mast

Hammerhead crane

Rotating service structure

Orbiter

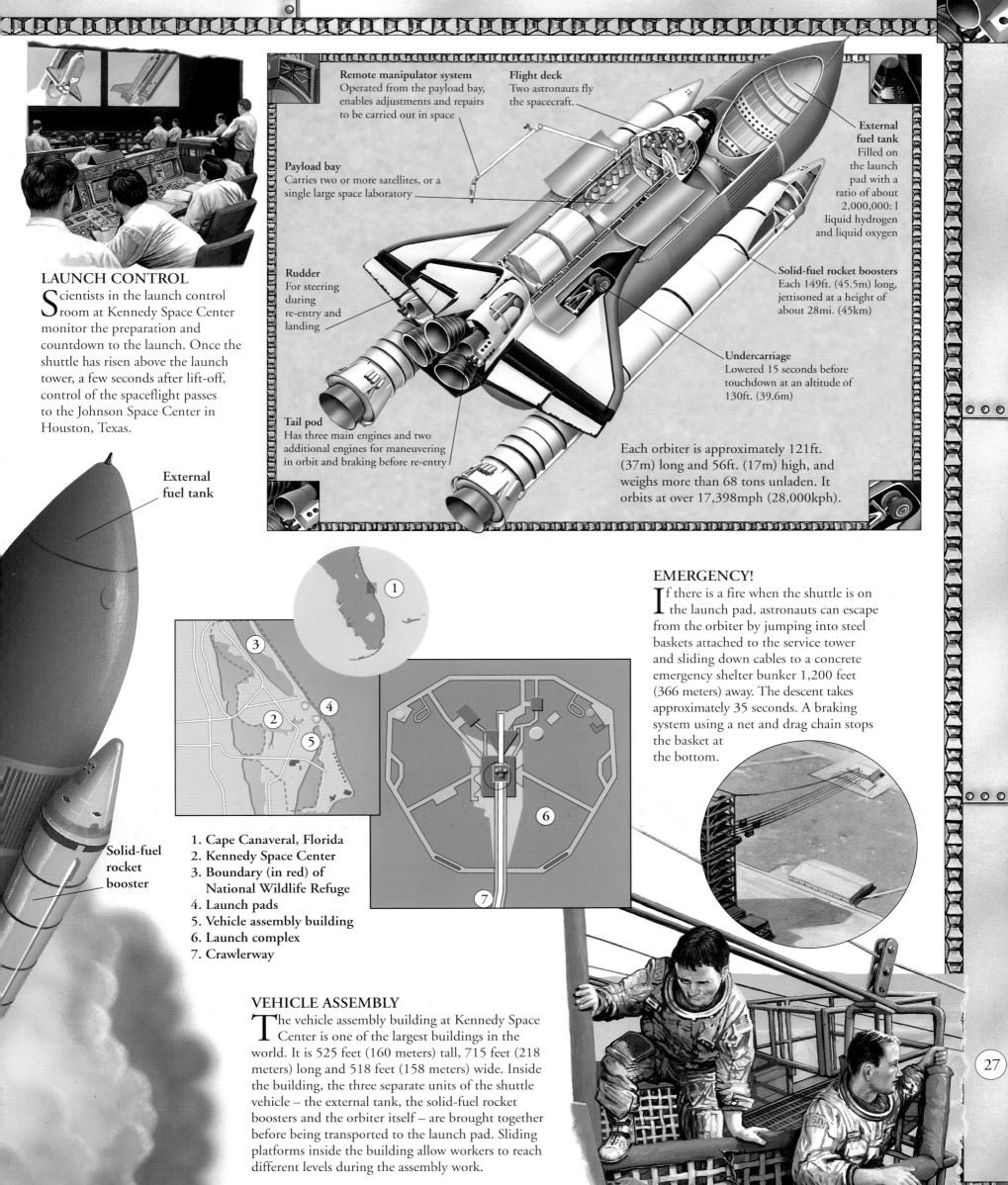

LAUNCH CONTROL

Scientists in the launch control room at Kennedy Space Center monitor the preparation and countdown to the launch. Once the shuttle has risen above the launch tower, a few seconds after lift-off, control of the spaceflight passes to the Johnson Space Center in Houston, Texas.

External fuel tank

Solid-fuel rocket booster

Remote manipulator system
Operated from the payload bay, enables adjustments and repairs to be carried out in space

Flight deck
Two astronauts fly the spacecraft.

Payload bay
Carries two or more satellites, or a single large space laboratory

Rudder
For steering during re-entry and landing

Tail pod
Has three main engines and two additional engines for maneuvering in orbit and braking before re-entry

External fuel tank
Filled on the launch pad with a ratio of about 2,000,000:1 liquid hydrogen and liquid oxygen

Solid-fuel rocket boosters
Each 149ft. (45.5m) long, jettisoned at a height of about 28mi. (45km)

Undercarriage
Lowered 15 seconds before touchdown at an altitude of 130ft. (39.6m)

Each orbiter is approximately 121ft. (37m) long and 56ft. (17m) high, and weighs more than 68 tons unladen. It orbits at over 17,398mph (28,000kph).

1. Cape Canaveral, Florida
2. Kennedy Space Center
3. Boundary (in red) of National Wildlife Refuge
4. Launch pads
5. Vehicle assembly building
6. Launch complex
7. Crawlerway

EMERGENCY!

If there is a fire when the shuttle is on the launch pad, astronauts can escape from the orbiter by jumping into steel baskets attached to the service tower and sliding down cables to a concrete emergency shelter bunker 1,200 feet (366 meters) away. The descent takes approximately 35 seconds. A braking system using a net and drag chain stops the basket at the bottom.

VEHICLE ASSEMBLY

The vehicle assembly building at Kennedy Space Center is one of the largest buildings in the world. It is 525 feet (160 meters) tall, 715 feet (218 meters) long and 518 feet (158 meters) wide. Inside the building, the three separate units of the shuttle vehicle – the external tank, the solid-fuel rocket boosters and the orbiter itself – are brought together before being transported to the launch pad. Sliding platforms inside the building allow workers to reach different levels during the assembly work.

27

Thames Barrier

"There was last night the greatest tide that ever was remembered in England to have been in this River, all Whitehall having been drowned."
Samuel Pepys's Diary,
December 7, 1663

London, England's capital city, stands beside the Thames River. Areas of the city near the river have been close to disaster at least twice in the twentieth century. In 1928, fourteen Londoners were drowned in floods. Then in 1953, floodwater along the riverbanks came only inches away from spilling over. The main threat of flooding comes from surges of water driven across the North Atlantic by cyclones. These surges usually pass north of Britain, but sometimes they sweep down the North Sea and into the Thames. Early in the 1970s, it was decided that London needed protection from possible floods. After 41 different schemes had been studied, the design of engineer Charles Draper was chosen.

In 1974, work started on a huge barrier across the Thames at Woolwich Reach, downstream from central London. The Barrier took eight years to complete. It consists of a series of steel gates that rest on the riverbed when they are not needed, allowing ships to pass freely. When there is a flood alert, the gates are closed (raised) to form a 1,706-foot (520-meter) wide wall of steel that holds back floodwater.

RISING WATERS

The Thames River's high-water level has risen by about 30 inches (75 centimeters) each century. Experts who keep a careful watch on sea levels predict that they are likely to rise by about 3 feet (1 meter) each century in the future.

1. Thames Flood Barrier
2. Houses of Parliament

Central pier

LONDON'S NIGHTMARE

The great North Sea surge of 1953, which drowned over 300 people along the east coast of England, brought London to the edge of a disaster like the one imagined above. At the last moment, the cyclone that created the surge swept away toward continental Europe, and the water lapping the tops of the Thames embankments dropped.

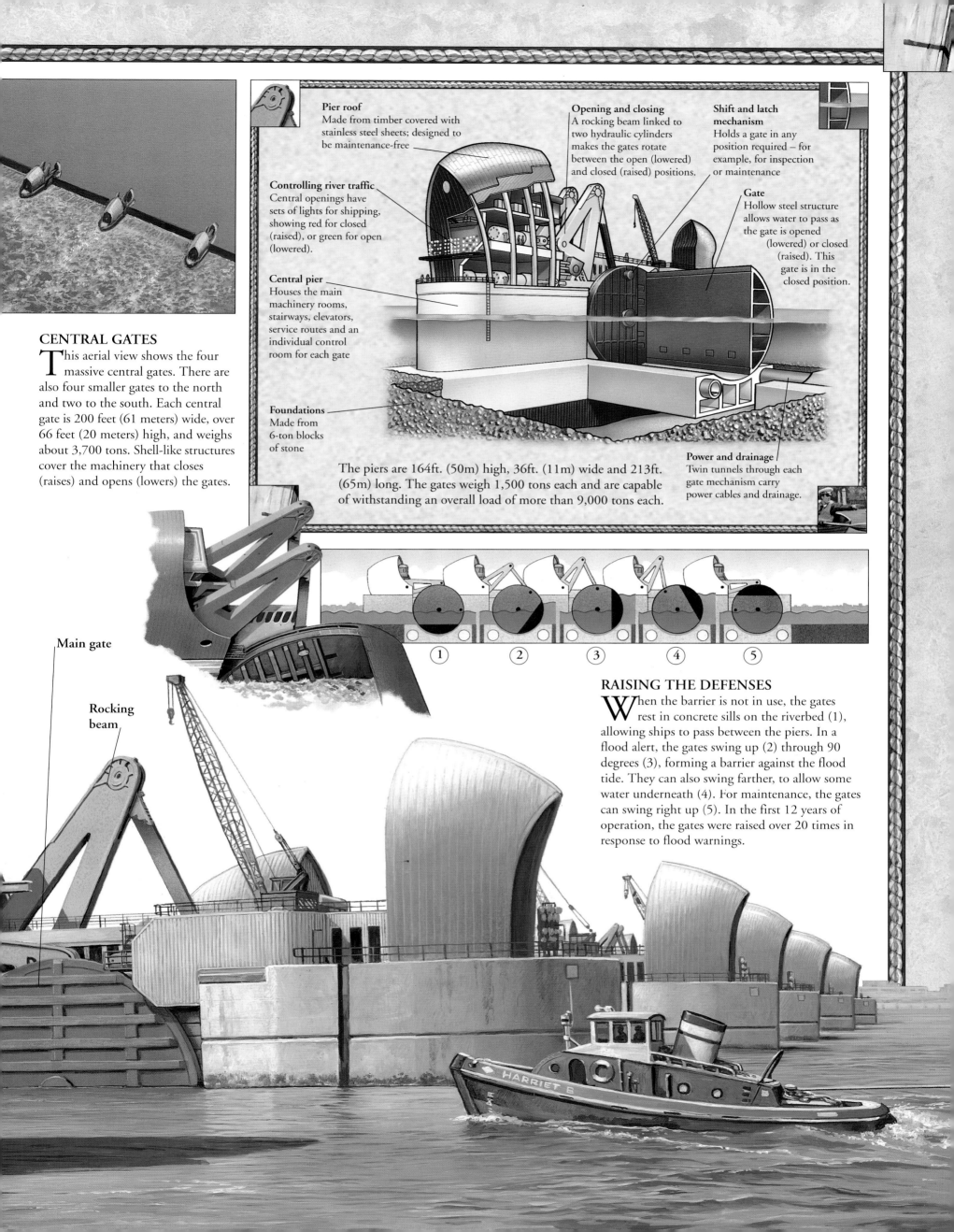

CENTRAL GATES

This aerial view shows the four massive central gates. There are also four smaller gates to the north and two to the south. Each central gate is 200 feet (61 meters) wide, over 66 feet (20 meters) high, and weighs about 3,700 tons. Shell-like structures cover the machinery that closes (raises) and opens (lowers) the gates.

Pier roof
Made from timber covered with stainless steel sheets; designed to be maintenance-free

Opening and closing
A rocking beam linked to two hydraulic cylinders makes the gates rotate between the open (lowered) and closed (raised) positions.

Shift and latch mechanism
Holds a gate in any position required – for example, for inspection or maintenance

Controlling river traffic
Central openings have sets of lights for shipping, showing red for closed (raised), or green for open (lowered).

Gate
Hollow steel structure allows water to pass as the gate is opened (lowered) or closed (raised). This gate is in the closed position.

Central pier
Houses the main machinery rooms, stairways, elevators, service routes and an individual control room for each gate

Foundations
Made from 6-ton blocks of stone

The piers are 164ft. (50m) high, 36ft. (11m) wide and 213ft. (65m) long. The gates weigh 1,500 tons each and are capable of withstanding an overall load of more than 9,000 tons each.

Power and drainage
Twin tunnels through each gate mechanism carry power cables and drainage.

Main gate

Rocking beam

① ② ③ ④ ⑤

RAISING THE DEFENSES

When the barrier is not in use, the gates rest in concrete sills on the riverbed (1), allowing ships to pass between the piers. In a flood alert, the gates swing up (2) through 90 degrees (3), forming a barrier against the flood tide. They can also swing farther, to allow some water underneath (4). For maintenance, the gates can swing right up (5). In the first 12 years of operation, the gates were raised over 20 times in response to flood warnings.

HARRIET B

Channel Tunnel

"It is done, and we who were there at the doing of it can now look back and wonder that it got done."

Alastair Morton, cochairman, Eurotunnel, 1994

The Channel Tunnel, linking England and France, carries passengers and vehicles by rail on a 31-mile (50-kilometer) journey that takes them under the English Channel. It was completed in 1993 after seven years of work, and was officially opened in 1994 by Queen Elizabeth II of the United Kingdom and President Mitterand of France. The tunnel is Europe's largest single piece of engineering work. It is in fact three tunnels: two main tunnels and a smaller service tunnel between them. Both the French and the English trains use one of the main tunnels to travel in one direction, and use the other main tunnel to travel in the other direction. The service tunnel was built first. The French and British engineers, working from each end, met in the middle on December 1, 1990. Cars, coaches and trucks travel through the tunnel on shuttle trains. They board and leave these at terminals that are linked to the major road systems of Britain and France. The train journey between the terminals takes just 35 minutes. Rail passengers can travel through the tunnel on high-speed trains that link London, Paris and Brussels, as well as other cities on the route.

CUTTING PICK

The tunnel-boring machine (or TBM) can be fitted with different kinds of cutterhead. For dry rock, picks are used. Each pick is made from hardened steel and cuts with a rocking action that provides the correct angle of attack for the cutting edge, while avoiding damage to the trailing edge.

LINING THE TUNNEL

The lining of the main tunnels and the service tunnel is made from curved segments of reinforced concrete. These were manufactured on land and brought to the site ready for use. Each ring of segments is about 5 feet (1.5 meters) long. The rings were built starting with the lowest segment, and ending with the placing of a smaller key segment – holding the ring in position – in the roof. The joints were then sealed with special cement.

Cutterhead

Shaft

BREAKTHROUGH

Excitement grew among tunnel workers during the autumn of 1990 as the French and British teams dug ever closer to each other. On December 1, they made the breakthrough and demolished the last few inches of rock, creating the first land route between England and France for 12 thousand years.

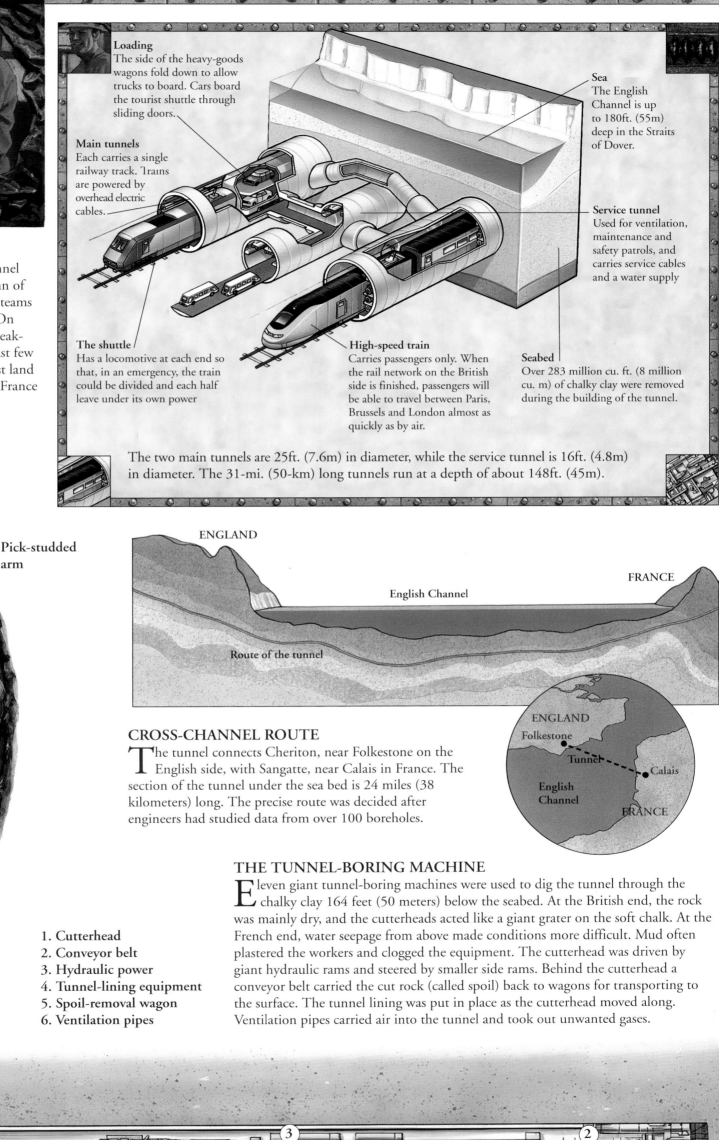

Loading
The side of the heavy-goods wagons fold down to allow trucks to board. Cars board the tourist shuttle through sliding doors.

Main tunnels
Each carries a single railway track. Trains are powered by overhead electric cables.

The shuttle
Has a locomotive at each end so that, in an emergency, the train could be divided and each half leave under its own power

High-speed train
Carries passengers only. When the rail network on the British side is finished, passengers will be able to travel between Paris, Brussels and London almost as quickly as by air.

Sea
The English Channel is up to 180ft. (55m) deep in the Straits of Dover.

Service tunnel
Used for ventilation, maintenance and safety patrols, and carries service cables and a water supply

Seabed
Over 283 million cu. ft. (8 million cu. m) of chalky clay were removed during the building of the tunnel.

The two main tunnels are 25ft. (7.6m) in diameter, while the service tunnel is 16ft. (4.8m) in diameter. The 31-mi. (50-km) long tunnels run at a depth of about 148ft. (45m).

Pick-studded arm

ENGLAND
FRANCE
English Channel
Route of the tunnel

CROSS-CHANNEL ROUTE

The tunnel connects Cheriton, near Folkestone on the English side, with Sangatte, near Calais in France. The section of the tunnel under the sea bed is 24 miles (38 kilometers) long. The precise route was decided after engineers had studied data from over 100 boreholes.

ENGLAND
Folkestone
Tunnel
Calais
English Channel
FRANCE

THE TUNNEL-BORING MACHINE

Eleven giant tunnel-boring machines were used to dig the tunnel through the chalky clay 164 feet (50 meters) below the seabed. At the British end, the rock was mainly dry, and the cutterheads acted like a giant grater on the soft chalk. At the French end, water seepage from above made conditions more difficult. Mud often plastered the workers and clogged the equipment. The cutterhead was driven by giant hydraulic rams and steered by smaller side rams. Behind the cutterhead a conveyor belt carried the cut rock (called spoil) back to wagons for transporting to the surface. The tunnel lining was put in place as the cutterhead moved along. Ventilation pipes carried air into the tunnel and took out unwanted gases.

1. Cutterhead
2. Conveyor belt
3. Hydraulic power
4. Tunnel-lining equipment
5. Spoil-removal wagon
6. Ventilation pipes

Mir Space Station

PEACE SIGN

The *Mir* emblem shows the space station against a background of Earth and stars, beneath the word *MIR*, which is Russian for "peace." The emblem is used on many items of equipment and on the crews' uniforms.

"As we came close, it looked like a white-winged seagull soaring above the world. Everything that contemporary technology can create is here."
Leonid Kizim, first commander of *Mir*, March 16, 1986

The *Mir* Space Station was launched in February 1986 by what was then the Soviet Union to study the long-term effects of living in space. It was designed so that its crew could live and work comfortably for long periods, and has even been described as a "space hotel." It has been occupied continuously by a succession of cosmonauts, some of whom have stayed for a year at a time. Since the launch of the base unit, new modules have been added, and linked in various positions, to enable various kinds of scientific experiments to be carried out. The *Kvant 1* module has specialized telescopes for studying space, while the *Kristall* module is a minifactory used to produce flawless semiconductor crystals for use in electronics.

Two kinds of spacecraft travel between Earth and *Mir*. Unmanned *Progress* craft deliver supplies and take away rubbish. Crew members arrive and depart on *Soyuz* spacecraft. In 1995 there was a different visitor: History was made when a United States space shuttle docked at the Russian space station.

WALKING IN SPACE

Crew members of *Mir* sometimes need to go outside the station to conduct experiments, inspect the modules or repair equipment. They put on space suits and a backpack. The backpack uses blasts of compressed air to help them move around. The cosmonauts remain tethered to the station so that they cannot float off into space.

THE ATMOSPHERE

To travel into space, spacecraft have to overcome the pull of Earth's gravity. That is why huge rockets, blasting upwards at 24,850 miles per hour (40,000 kilometers per hour), are needed to launch a spacecraft. They must travel up through the Earth's atmosphere for over 125 miles (200 kilometers) before they are free of gravity and can go into orbit.

Base unit

Kvant 2

Kristall module

200

180

160

140

120

100

80

60

40

20

0

Height in kilometres

TIME TO EAT

Food for the *Mir* crew comes in cans or flexible packs similar to toothpaste tubes. Prepacked cookies and bread are moistened to avoid crumbs, which would fly everywhere in the weightless conditions. Each food pack contains its own fork and spoon.

Solar panels

Kvant 1

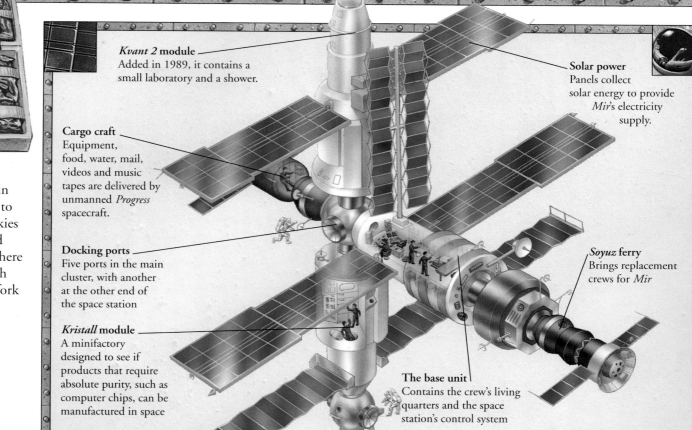

Kvant 2 module
Added in 1989, it contains a small laboratory and a shower.

Solar power
Panels collect solar energy to provide *Mir*'s electricity supply.

Cargo craft
Equipment, food, water, mail, videos and music tapes are delivered by unmanned *Progress* spacecraft.

Docking ports
Five ports in the main cluster, with another at the other end of the space station

Kristall module
A minifactory designed to see if products that require absolute purity, such as computer chips, can be manufactured in space

Soyuz **ferry**
Brings replacement crews for *Mir*

The base unit
Contains the crew's living quarters and the space station's control system

Mir's base unit is 43ft. (13m) long and weighs 21 tons. Extra space is provided by two *Kvant* modules and the *Kristall* module.

BEDTIME

Crew members are weightless while they are on board *Mir*, so they can sleep in any position. In the living quarters, visitors each have their own small cabin equipped with a sleeping bag attached to the wall. They zip themselves up to the neck, so that they don't float around while they are asleep. The crew member settling down for the night here is Helen Sharman, who in 1991 was chosen from hundreds of applicants to be the first British cosmonaut. She traveled to *Mir* in *Soyuz TM12.*

Proton **rocket**

Soyuz **ferry**

Kvant 1

Base unit

Earth

LAUNCHING MIR

The base unit of *Mir* was launched on February 20, 1986. The 21-ton space station was lifted into orbit by a *Proton* rocket that was specially designed to carry heavy loads into space. The *Soyuz* ferry enabled the crew to return to Earth.

Gullfaks C

FLARE STACK

A buildup of excess gas from an oil rig's operations is a potential fire hazard. The excess gas is burned off on a flare stack sited well away from the production and living areas.

"Geologically speaking, the development and operation of the Gullfaks field is a great challenge. The company was confronted with the most complicated reservoir so far considered for production in the North Sea."
Statoil Information Department, 1990

TAKING THE OIL ASHORE

Oil is transported away from Gullfaks C by tankers. They moor at special loading buoys close to the platform. Oil is stored in the rig's base and piped to the mooring buoys. Gullfaks C can produce 250,000 barrels of oil a day.

Gullfaks is the name of a Norwegian oilfield in the North Sea between Britain and mainland Europe. Rising out of the sea above the oilfield is the Gullfaks C gas and oil production platform. Gullfaks C consists of a steel framework attached to four huge concrete pillars and a base, which rests on the seabed 712 feet (217 meters) below the surface. It is 1,148 feet (350 meters) from the seabed to the highest point of the rig. The framework is fitted with working and living quarters for a crew of 330. It also supports production equipment, derricks for loading and unloading goods, and a helicopter pad.

Natural gas was discovered under the North Sea in 1959, followed by oil in 1970, and since then numerous production platforms have been installed. Gullfaks C is the largest platform to date.

TALLER THAN THE EIFFEL TOWER

Standing 1,148 feet (350 meters) from the seabed to its highest point, Gullfaks C is 164 feet (50 meters) taller than the famous Eiffel Tower in Paris, France.

Accommodation block

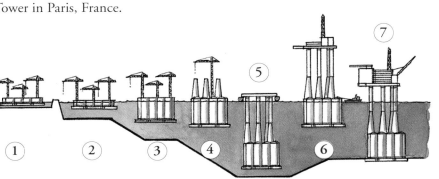

Concrete supporting pillars

ASSEMBLING THE OIL RIG

There are seven key stages to erecting an oil rig. The hollow concrete supports, or caissons, that form the base of the rig are built in dry dock, towed out to sea and submerged. The rest of the rig is then added.

1. The caissons are built in dry dock.
2. The dock is flooded and the base is towed by tug into sheltered water.
3. As construction continues, the caissons are lowered by pumping in more water.
4. When the water level reaches the top of the caissons, concrete pillars are added.
5. The platform is built on top of the concrete pillars.
6. Water is then partly pumped out of the caissons, and the rig is towed by tug into its final position.
7. The caissons are filled with water and sunk to rest on the seabed.

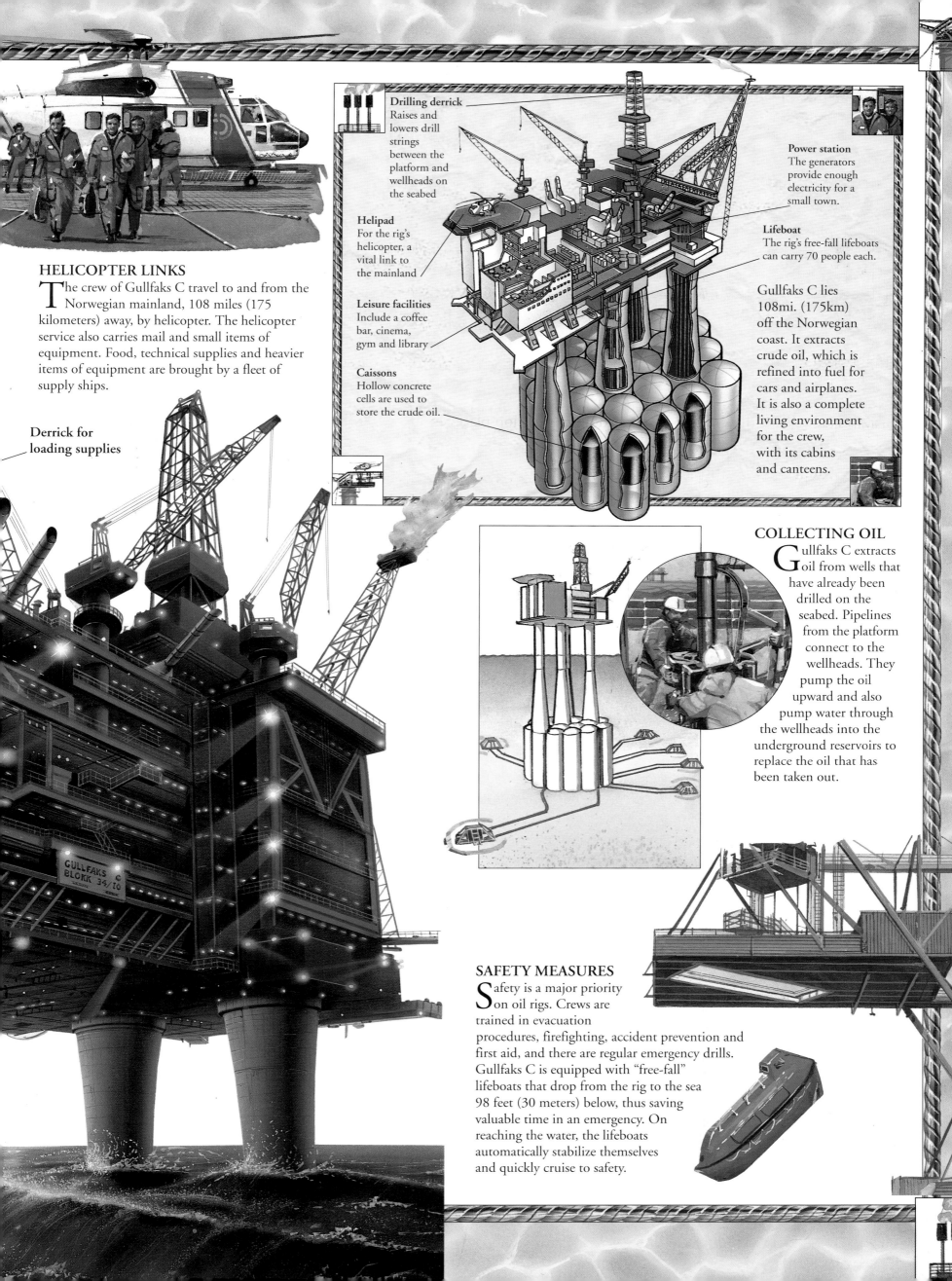

HELICOPTER LINKS

The crew of Gullfaks C travel to and from the Norwegian mainland, 108 miles (175 kilometers) away, by helicopter. The helicopter service also carries mail and small items of equipment. Food, technical supplies and heavier items of equipment are brought by a fleet of supply ships.

Derrick for loading supplies

Drilling derrick
Raises and lowers drill strings between the platform and wellheads on the seabed

Helipad
For the rig's helicopter, a vital link to the mainland

Leisure facilities
Include a coffee bar, cinema, gym and library

Caissons
Hollow concrete cells are used to store the crude oil.

Power station
The generators provide enough electricity for a small town.

Lifeboat
The rig's free-fall lifeboats can carry 70 people each.

Gullfaks C lies 108mi. (175km) off the Norwegian coast. It extracts crude oil, which is refined into fuel for cars and airplanes. It is also a complete living environment for the crew, with its cabins and canteens.

COLLECTING OIL

Gullfaks C extracts oil from wells that have already been drilled on the seabed. Pipelines from the platform connect to the wellheads. They pump the oil upward and also pump water through the wellheads into the underground reservoirs to replace the oil that has been taken out.

SAFETY MEASURES

Safety is a major priority on oil rigs. Crews are trained in evacuation procedures, firefighting, accident prevention and first aid, and there are regular emergency drills. Gullfaks C is equipped with "free-fall" lifeboats that drop from the rig to the sea 98 feet (30 meters) below, thus saving valuable time in an emergency. On reaching the water, the lifeboats automatically stabilize themselves and quickly cruise to safety.

White-knuckle ride

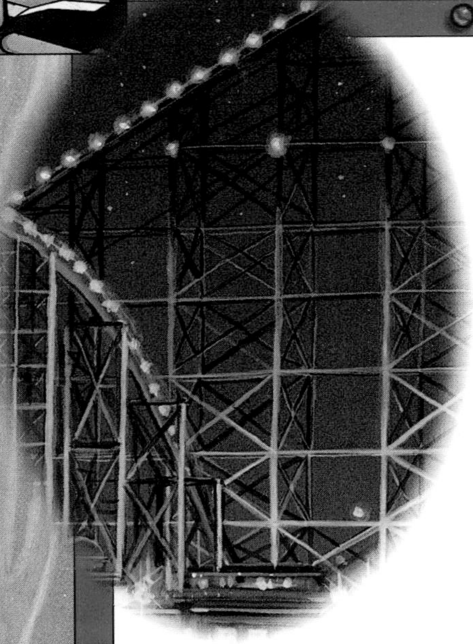

At 235 feet (nearly 72 meters) high, the Pepsi Max Big One at Blackpool Pleasure Beach, England, is the world's tallest rollercoaster. Its three trains carry visitors for a stomach-churning two-minute ride of over 5,249 feet (1,600 meters) at speeds of up to 84.5 miles per hour (136 kilometers per hour). Opened in 1994, the Big One is a wonder of structural engineering. Engineers had to calculate precisely the forces exerted on the track and the steel framework supporting it as the trains hurtle around the Big One's tight vertical and horizontal bends. Because of these forces, passengers feel up to four times heavier than their true weight at a number of points during the ride.

At full capacity, trains leave the station at intervals of 63 seconds. This amazing ride can be enjoyed by a total of 1,700 people every hour.

LIGHTING UP

In addition to the floodlights that illuminate the Big One after dark, aircraft warning beacons are mounted on the structure. These are needed because of the ride's height and the fact that Blackpool's airport is not far away.

PUTTING ON THE BRAKES

There are four braking units like the one shown below, one at the station and three on the track itself. One half of the brake unit remains in a fixed position, and the other half moves. As each car passes over the brake unit, the moving part clamps onto a fin attached to the base of the car between the wheels. The brakes are used to reduce the train's speed or to stop the train.

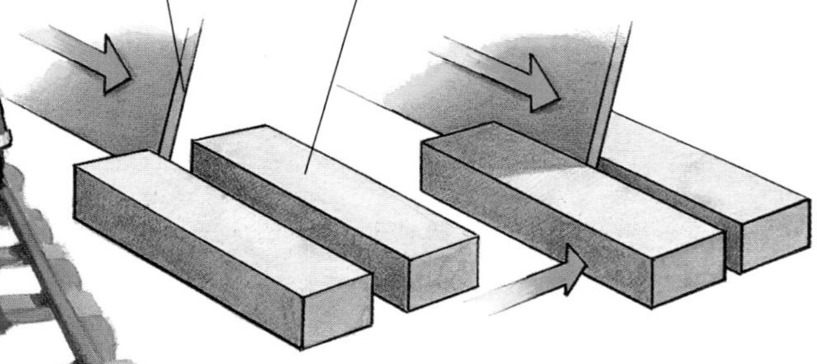

Fin attached to base of car

Brake unit

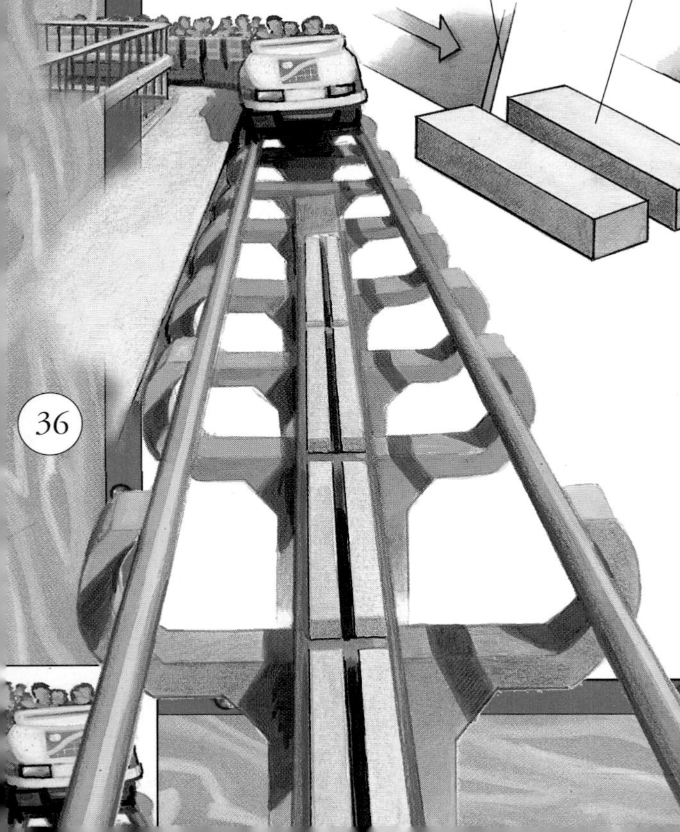

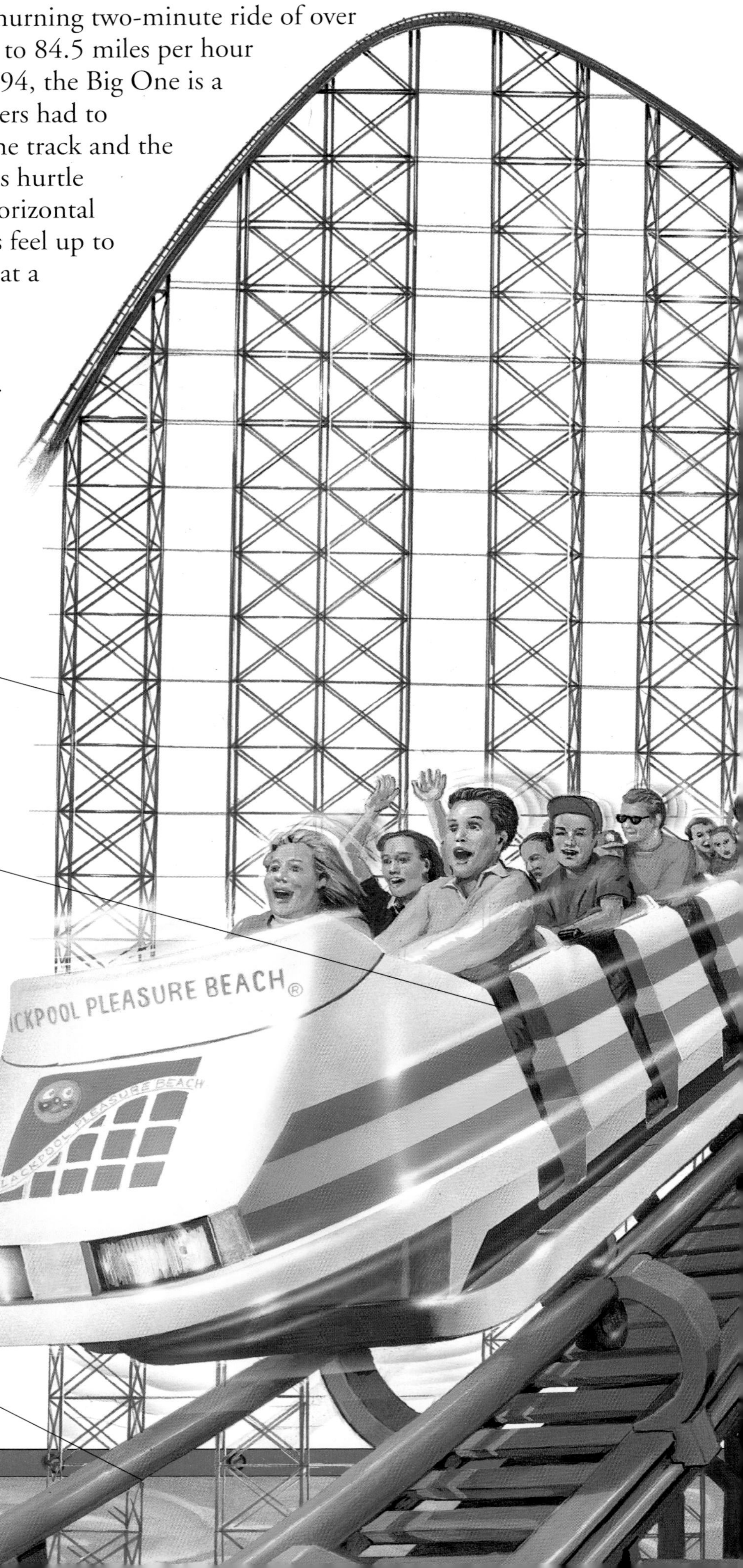

Steel stanchion

Seats with safety bars

Spotlight

Track rail

BLACKPOOL PLEASURE BEACH®

VITAL STATISTICS

The ride is supported by 94 monopods and 237 stanchions. To overcome the effects of corrosion from salt and sand in the sea air, protective paint is regularly applied.

Ride takes about two minutes

Over 60,000 bolts used in construction

2,600 tons of steel were used, equal to 40mi. (64km) if laid end to end

376,733sq. ft. (35,000sq. m) of surface area were painted with five coats of paint

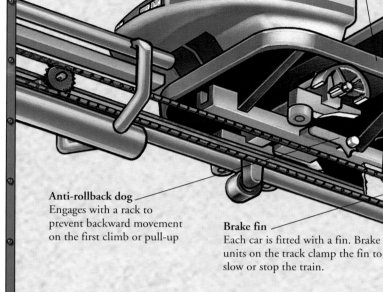

Train lighting
Each train has battery-powered spotlights front and rear.

Chassis
Consists of a longitudinal spar supporting four triangular sections

Seating
A train can carry 30 passengers, all protected by locking safety bars.

Wheels
Four wheels on each car ride on round-sectioned running rails, and four smaller wheels run beneath the rails.

Anti-rollback dog
Engages with a rack to prevent backward movement on the first climb or pull-up

Brake fin
Each car is fitted with a fin. Brake units on the track clamp the fin to slow or stop the train.

The cars of each Pepsi Max Big One train are permanently coupled, giving an overall length of 52ft. (15.9m).

ALL THE FUN OF THE FAIR

The 235-feet (72-metre)-high Big One towers above all the other rollercoaster rides in the park.

USING GRAVITY

At the top of a slope, a stationary rollercoaster train (1) has energy. This energy, called potential gravitational energy, can be used to move downhill at speed. Once the train starts moving down the slope (2), this turns into the kinetic energy of motion, which carries the train to the top of the next slope (3). There it changes back to potential energy. The top of each slope has to be slightly lower than the one before it because the train loses some of its energy to friction against the track and to air resistance.

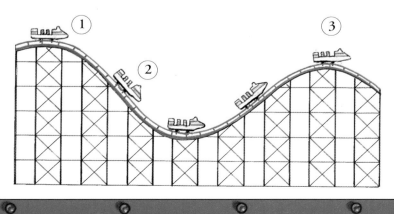

UPHILL CLIMB

At the starting station, the train attaches to a moving chain that pulls it up the first steep incline. Two devices called chain dogs on the second and fourth cars engage with the chain, and as the chain moves the train is pulled up the incline. At the crest of the first drop, a release mechanism on the track detaches the chain dogs from the chain, and the train hurtles downhill at an angle of 65 degrees.

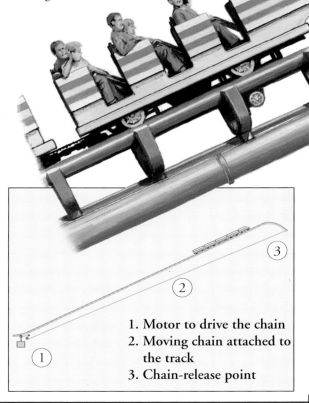

1. Motor to drive the chain
2. Moving chain attached to the track
3. Chain-release point

GLOSSARY

amphitheater
An open structure built for large numbers of spectators to watch gladiatorial contests and other entertainment. Amphitheaters were built in many of the cities of the Roman empire.

amplify
To make louder and stronger.

antenna
A metal rod or wire used to receive or transmit electronic signals.

aqueduct
A bridge-like structure designed to carry water overhead.

Art Deco
A modern, highly colored, streamlined style of decoration that was developed during the 1920s and was widely used on buildings, furniture, furnishing materials and domestic goods such as plates and cups.

awning
A temporary roof made of canvas or other cloth that can be placed in position and removed as required.

azimuth
An imaginary line drawn from the point in the sky immediately above an observer's head to the horizon.

beacon
A fire lit at a highly visible point, usually to pass on a warning about enemy troop movements. Chains of beacons, lit in turn, could carry messages over long distances.

borehole
A hole drilled in the ground by engineers to obtain a core of the underlying rock, which can then be studied to find out what lies beneath the ground surface.

box
An open-sided enclosure in a theatre or an amphitheater for use by important spectators.

buoy
Any float anchored at sea to mark an underwater hazard or for use as a mooring.

buttressed
Any structure supported by pillars of brick or stone. A flying buttress is a special kind of supporting arch or partial arch that is most commonly seen in cathedrals.

caisson
A watertight case of metal or concrete, often used as a foundation for underwater structures.

cantilever
A beam, firmly anchored and weighted down at one end, that is able to support another beam at its free end.

capstone
The topmost stone of a structure (such as a pyramid), often ornately decorated.

cast iron
A type of iron that is run into molds when it is molten (hot and liquid) and then allowed to set.

cathedral
A very large Christian church that contains the throne of a bishop.

chain dog
A revolving cog wheel attached to a vehicle; it engages with a chain and provides the driving force for the vehicle.

china clay
A fine white powder extracted from the ground up for use in making pottery.

chisel
A hand tool with a stone or metal end, used to shape stone or wood.

compressed-air drilling machine
A drill (sometimes called a pneumatic drill) driven by compressed air which, as it expands, provides the power to drill holes in rock.

concrete
A mixture of sand, gravel and cement that is used in construction.

conveyor belt
A continuously moving endless belt that carries waste material from an excavation to trucks for transport to a disposal site.

corrosion
Damage caused to metal structures by the chemical action of the atmosphere or sea water. Rust, the reddish-brown deposit that affects iron, is an example of corrosion.

counterweight
An extra weight that is fitted to a heavy object to balance the object's weight and to help control its movement.

cross-braced
Fitted with diagonal spars of metal to give added strength to a structure.

crude oil
Thick, syrupy oil that is pumped from an oil well. Crude oil must be "cracked," or processed, to remove impurities and separate different thicknesses of oil for various uses.

cutterhead
A mechanically driven revolving tool at the front of a drilling machine that can be fitted with a variety of cutting picks, drills and teeth to perform different cutting and drilling tasks.

cyclone
A system of winds that revolves around a low-pressure area. The winds can reach very high speeds and sometimes cause damage to structures and trees, even large ones.

Declaration of Independence
An agreement signed on July 4, 1776 by the founders of the United States of America. It announced that the country was no longer a British possession, and stated the rules by which the United States would be governed.

derrick
A fixed crane used to raise and lower drill tubes over an oil well.

dolerite
A hard rock, sometimes containing fragments of a glass-like substance, used in the Iron Age to make cutting tools.

dynamite
A safe explosive based on nitroglycerine and invented by the Swedish chemist Alfred Nobel in 1866. It is detonated using a lit fuse or by a charge of high-voltage electricity.

embankment
An artificial riverbank built of earth or stone to prevent water from flooding nearby land.

emplacement
A small structure that contains a cannon or other large mechanical weapon and gives protection to the gun crew that mans it.

encoder
A device that changes electronic signals into a form in which they can be transmitted or interpreted.

generator
A machine for producing electricity by rotating a coil of wire in a magnetic field. The energy to drive the generator is provided by steam pressure from an oil, coal, gas or nuclear fuel furnace, or by wind, wave or solar power.

girder
A beam of iron or steel used as a support in structures, usually formed into a T or L shape to give added strength.

gold leaf
A decorative material made by beating gold (a soft metal) into very thin sheets.

granite
A hard volcanic rock that resists the effects of weathering and corrosion.

gravity
A force on the Earth that acts on objects close to the Earth and pulls them towards its center. Rockets used in space launches have to be powerful enough to enable spacecraft to overcome the force of gravity and reach space, where gravity is no longer effective.

gunpowder
A mixture of chemicals and charcoal invented by the ancient Chinese. It was the only known explosive until the 19th century.

hand tool
A tool that is operated without the use of machinery. Hand tools are still used, mostly to cut and shape wood and stone.

hanger
A steel cable suspended from the arch of a bridge to support the bridge's deck.

hard hat
A protective helmet worn by construction workers to shield them.

headroom
The space underneath the deck of a bridge or the roof of a tunnel that enables ships or automobile traffic to pass through.

herald
An official in a Roman amphitheater who made announcements at the start of the program and helped control the crowd.

hurricane
A storm with winds exceeding 75mph (120kph).

hydraulic
Operated by the pressure of a liquid such as oil or water.

inscription
Words cut into the stone of a monument, often recording when and by whom it was built.

limestone
A stone that has been used for building from the earliest times because it can be cut and shaped using only simple tools.

lock
A device that enables vessels using waterways to change levels. The vessel moves into a position on the waterway, and watertight gates are shut in front of and behind it. The water level between the gates is then raised or lowered to match the level in the next lock or stretch of water. The gates in front of the vessel are opened and it moves forward at the new level.

mallet
A hammer, usually with a wooden head, used to tap or cut stone or bricks into position.

marble
A hard, durable form of limestone that can be carved and polished.

module
A section of a building or structure that is made in a factory and then transported to the site where it is going to be used.

mooring
A place where a ship or airship can be anchored or tethered. Airships can not take off or land like winged aircraft. They moor at tall masts, and passengers and crew embark or disembark while the airship is tied to the mast by ropes.

mortar
A mixture of lime, sand and water used to join stones or bricks together. It is applied wet, and when it dries it makes a hard bond between adjoining surfaces.

mummy
A dead body (usually human but sometimes animal) soaked in oils and other chemicals and then wrapped tightly in cloth to preserve it. The ancient Egyptians mummified their kings in the belief that this would ensure life after death.

murmillo gladiator
One of the classes of gladiators who fought before audiences in the Roman Empire. Murmillo gladiators were heavily armed, with helmets, swords and shields.

navigable
A body of water, natural or artificial, that is sufficiently wide and deep to be used by ships.

optical telescope
A telescope that gathers light from a distant object and presents an image to the observer through a system of lenses and mirrors.

parabolic
Bowl-shaped.

parapet
A wall built along the top of fortifications to give protection to soldiers.

payload
Cargo.

pedestal
The base supporting a column, pillar or statue.

persecution
The deliberate, systematic ill treatment of people by their government or society.

pre-stressed concrete
A type of strengthened concrete that is poured over wires which are then tightened before the concrete hardens. The set concrete holds the stressed wires in place and this gives added strength. Pre-stressed concrete was invented by a French engineer, Eugene Freyssinet, in 1930.

pulley
A grooved wheel used with a rope to lift heavy loads with minimum effort. Pulleys may be fixed in a block attached to a structure, or movable as in a crane or derrick.

reinforced concrete
Concrete strengthened by being poured over a network of metal wire. It was invented by a French gardener, Joseph Monier, in 1868 as a way of strengthening artificial ponds and flowerpots.

reservoir
A large natural or artificial store for liquids.

restoration
Work carried out on a structure to return it to its original condition.

retiarius gladiator
One of the classes of Roman gladiators. Retiarius gladiators wore only a short tunic or apron and carried a three-pronged spear and a net. Their aim was to trap their opponents in the net and then kill them with the spear.

rivet
A device for fastening two pieces of metal together. A rivet consists of a length of steel that is passed through holes in the pieces of metal. The ends of the pieces are then beaten flat to make the fastening.

roller coaster
A high-speed fairground ride that carries passengers in open carriages along a very steeply inclined and tightly curved track.

semiconductor
A solid substance that conducts electricity at high temperatures but acts as an insulator at low temperatures. Semiconductors are used in many modern electronic devices such as radios, televisions and videos.

skyscraper
A tall modern building. There is no definition of how tall a building must be to be called a skyscraper, but the Home Insurance Building in Chicago, built in 1885 and only ten storeys high, is regarded as the world's first.

spoil
The general term for waste material from construction and engineering works.

square
An L-shaped tool used by construction workers and carpenters to check right angles.

subreflector
A part of a radio telescope which collects radio signals bounced off the parabolic reflector. It focuses them before passing them on to the radio receiver.

surge
A sea condition created when strong winds blowing onshore prevent the high tide from receding, so that the next high tide adds to the previous one.

terracotta
Baked clay.

tunneling shield
A tool used to protect workers building a tunnel. It consists of a steel cylinder with rotating cutting tools at its closed front end and metal sections behind, forming the closure.

vaulted
Supported by a series of arches radiating from a central point.

ventilation
Any method of supplying fresh air and extracting stale air and poisonous gases.

weightless
A person or object that is temporarily not affected by gravity. Spacecraft and their crews are weightless once they have escaped from the Earth's gravitational pull.

wellhead
A fixture attached to the seabed at the top of a borehole and connected by pipeline to an oil production platform. Pumps at the wellhead carry crude oil to the platform and return water to the well to replace the oil taken out.

winch
A method of raising or lowering heavy loads by turning a wheel which carries a rope.

wrought iron
Iron that is compressed by being passed through rollers while it is still semi-molten (very hot and semi-liquid). This process increases its toughness and resistance to corrosion.

INDEX